Death Valley Wildflowers

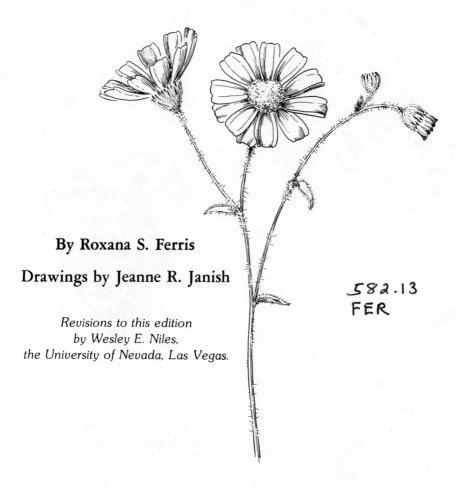

By Roxana S. Ferris

Drawings by Jeanne R. Janish

*Revisions to this edition
by Wesley E. Niles,
the University of Nevada, Las Vegas.*

Death Valley Natural History Association

Death Valley, California

Published by
Death Valley Natural History Association

The Death Valley Natural History Association is a non-profit educational organization dedicated to the preservation and interpretation of the natural and human history of Death Valley National Monument in cooperation with the National Park Service.

Death Valley Natural History Association
Second Revised Edition, 1981

Printed by
Chalfant Press, Inc.
Bishop, California

All Americans, whoever and wherever
they may be, share in that great
heritage which is represented by our
National Park System—our scenery
and our historic shrines. As our
vacation lands, they bring enjoyment
and refreshment of mind, body and
spirit to millions of Americans
each year.

ACKNOWLEDGEMENTS

I wish to thank all those who have helped me in the preparation of this booklet. Most especially I wish to express my gratitude to the personnel of the Death Valley National Monument who have aided both the author and the illustrator in so many ways during field work on this project.

In addition to field work, many books and pamphlets have been consulted. Of these, two have been especially helpful: F. V. Coville, *Botany of the Death Valley Expedition* published in 1893; and W. B. McDougal, *Check List of the Plants of Death Valley National Monument* published in mimeograph form in 1945. Four other books have been consulted extensively for source material: Abrams and Ferris, *Illustrated Flora of the Pacific States;* Jaeger, *Desert Wild Flowers;* Jepson, *A Flora of California;* Munz, *A California Flora.* The first volume of *Intermountain Flora* by Cronquist, A. Holmgren, N. Holmgren and Reveal was published in 1972. When this work is completed, it will be a most useful source book for the Death Valley area.

Roxana S. Ferris

Revisions incorporated in this edition are based, in part, on P. A. Munz' *A Flora of Southern California,* 1974.

LIST OF ILLUSTRATED SPECIES BY FAMILIES

Puffball family (Lycoperdiaceae)
  Podaxis pistillaris
Fern family (Polypodiaceae)
  Adiantum capillus-veneris
  Pellaea breweri
Pine family (Pinaceae)
  Pinus flexilis
  Pinus monophylla
  Pinus longaeva
Cypress family (Cupressaceae)
  Juniperus osteosperma
Ephedra family (Ephedraceae)
  Ephedra funerea
  Ephedra viridis
  Ephedra nevadensis
Crowfoot family (Ranunculaceae)
  Delphinium parishii
  Aquilegia shockleyi
Lizards-tail family (Saururaceae)
  Anemopsis californica
Mallow family (Malvaceae)
  Sphaeralcea ambigua
  Eremalche rotundifolia
Flax family (Linaceae)
  Linum lewisii
Caltrop family (Zygophyllaceae)
  Larrea tridentata
Spurge family (Euphorbiaceae)
  Euphorbia albomarginata
  Euphorbia parishii
Loasa family (Loasaceae)
  Mentzelia reflexa
  Mentzelia albicaulis
  Eucnide urens

Poppy family (Papaveraceae)
  Arctomecon merriamii
  Eschscholzia glyptosperma
  Argemone munita argentea
Caper family (Capparidaceae)
  Oxystylis lutea
  Cleomella obtusifolia
Mustard family (Brassicaceae)
  Stanleya elata
  Stanleya pinnata
  Caulanthus crassicaulis
  Arabis glaucovalvula
Cactus family (Cactaceae)
  Opuntia echinocarpa
  Opuntia basilaris
  Optuntia erinacea
  Echinocereus engelmannii
  Echinocactus polycephalus
Buckwheat family (Polygonaceae)
  Gilmania luteola
  Chorizanthe rigida
  Eriogonum inflatum
  Eriogonum brachypodum
  Eriogonum rixfordii
  Eriogonum nidularium
  Eriogonum panamintense
  Eriogonum fasciculatum polifolium
Goosefoot family (Chenopodiaceae)
  Atriplex canescens
  Atriplex hymenelytra
  Atriplex confertifolia
  Grayia spinosa
  Allenrolfea occidentalis
  Suaeda torreyana
Amaranth family (Amaranthaceae)
  Tidestromia oblongifolia

Four-o'clock family (Nyctaginaceae
  Abronia villosa
  Boerhaavia annulata
Olive family (Oleaceae)
  Menodora spinescens
Milkweed family (Asclepiadaceae)
  Asclepias erosa
Morning-glory family (Convolvulaceae)
  Cuscuta indecora
  Cuscuta denticulata
  Cuscuta nevadensis
Phlox family (Polemoniaceae)
  Phlox longifolia
  Gilia cana triceps
  Gilia filiformis
  Langloisia punctata
  Leptodactylon pungens
Waterleaf family (Hydrophyllaceae)
  Phacelia vallis-mortae
  Phacelia crenulata
  Phacelia perityloides
  Phacelia calthiflora
  Phacelia fremontii
  Nama demissum
Borage family (Boraginaceae)
  Cryptantha confertiflora
  Cryptantha utahensis
Potato family (Solanaceae)
  Datura meteloides
  Nicotiana trigonophylla
Figwort family (Scorphulariaceae)
  Mimulus bigelovii
  Minulus rupicola
  Penstemon fruticiformis
  Penstemon floridus austinii
  Penstemon bridgesii
  Maurandya petrophila
  Mohavea breviflora
  Antirrhinum filipes
  Castilleja chromosa
  Castilleja linariaefolia
Broomrape family (Orobanchaceae)
  Orobanche cooperi
Mint family (Lamiaceae)
  Salazaria mexicana
  Salvia funerea
  Salvia dorrii
  Salvia pachyphylla
Rose family (Rosaceae)
  Chamaebatiaria millefolium
  Cowania mexicana stansburiana
  Cercocarpus ledifolius
  Rosa woodsii gratissima
Pea family (Fabaceae)
  Prosopis glandulosa torreyana
  Cassia armata
  Lupinus flavoculatus
  Lupinus arizonicus
  Lotus rigidus
  Psorothamnus fremontii
  Astragalus layneae
  Astragalus coccineus
  Astragalus funereus

Evening-primrose family (Onagraceae)
  Oenothera caespitosa marginata
  Camissonia boothii condensata
  Camissonia cardiophylla
  Camissonia brevipes
  Camissonia claviformis
Mistletoe family (Loranthaceae)
  Phoradendron californicum
  Phoradendron bolleanum densum
Rue family (Rutaceae)
  Thamnosma montana
Maple family (Aceraceae)
  Acer glabrum
Carrot family (Apiaceae)
  Cymopterus gilmanii
  Lomatium parryi
Honeysuckle family (Caprifoliaceae)
  Symphoricarpos longiflorus
Gourd family (Cucurbitaceae)
  Cucurbita palmata
Sunflower family (Asteraceae)
  Viguiera reticulata
  Viguiera multiflora nevadensis
  Enceliopsis argophylla grandiflora
  Encelia farinosa
  Encelia virginensis actonii
  Geraea canescens
  Bebbia juncea aspera
  Hymenoclea salsola
  Ambrosia dumosa
  Chaenactis carphoclinia
  Gutierrezia sarothrae
  Gutierrezia microcephala
  Amphipappus fremontii
  Acamptopappus shockleyi
  Chrysothamnus paniculatus
  Chrysothamnus nauseosus
  Xylorhiza tortifolia
  Artemisia tridentata
  Artemisia spinescens
  Psathyrotes ramosissima
  Peucephyllum schottii
  Tessaria sericea
  Brickellia arguta
  Cirsium mohavense
  Hecastocleis shockleyi
  Malacothrix glabrata
  Stephanomeria pauciflora
  Calycoseris wrightii
  Anisocoma acaulis
  Atrichoseris platyphylla
Lily family (Liliaceae)
  Calochortus flexuosus
  Calochortus kennedyi
Orchid family (Orchidaceae)
  Epipactis gigantea
Rush family (Juncaceae)
  Juncus cooperi
Sedge family (Cyperaceae)
  Scirpus americanus
Grass family (Poaceae)
  Erioneuron pulchellum
  Sporobolus airoides

To see a world in a grain of sand,

And heaven in a wild-flower,

Hold infinity in the palm of your hand,

And eternity in an hour.

—William Blake

INTRODUCTION

Death Valley National Monument is a vast area with much diversity in climate, in soil, and also in altitudinal range (282 feet below sea level to above 11,000 feet). The physiographical features that one can see in the approximately 2,000,000 acres that are included within the borders of the monument are most varied. As far as plants are concerned, all these diversities offer endless possibilities for different types of growing things. The distance between the "lowest spot in the United States" and Telescope Peak, which is often snow-covered, is only 18 air miles. The distance by land, of course, is greater and it includes many types of plant habitats. If you were to walk instead of fly between the two points mentioned, you might see, in season, two-thirds of the kinds of plants growing in Death Valley National Monument. A precise count of the number of species found in the monument is yet to be made. In 1945 the number was estimated to be between 600 and 700 species and varieties. Probably between 900 and 1,000 would be a more nearly correct figure.

"Will the wildflowers be good this year?" is one of the first questions that comes to mind when planning a trip to Death Valley. To be sure, a few stray flowering annuals and shrubs can be seen here and there, even in the heat of the summer—ones that have gotten enough moisture to exist from the trickles of water that come down the alluvial fans after summer showers. In fact, some flowers can be found almost any month of the year. The best time to see a spring floral display on the valley floor and alluvial fans is in those years when the rainfall is two or three times the average 1.65 inches per year. A deluge in late October with no more rain through the cold winter months does not bring out the flowers as do the rains that are nicely spaced through the winter and into the warmer spring weather. With the ideal conditions one may see great stretches of desertgold, clumps of sandverbena and phacelia, and other plants that make bright patches of color. In normal and even in dry years there are some flowers in the spring season. It is well to remember that we are speaking of annual plants, and they are short-lived. With just a few hot spring days, the flower show is over. No wonder desert plants of this type are known as "ephemerals" (short-lived). There may be a second crop of plants from the seeds that ripened in the spring, if there are summer and fall showers to start them growing. In the high canyons of the ranges surrounding the valley, where growing conditions are not so tough, the annuals live longer.

But what about the shrubs and shrubby perennials of the valley floor and alluvial fans that must survive the intense heat of one summer season and keep on living into future seasons? (Soil temperatures as high as 201° F. at GROUND LEVEL have been recorded.) There are two general types of vegetation to consider: plants of the washes and larger drainage areas where the water table is high enough for the shrubs to derive some benefit from it; plants of alluvial fans and lower slopes where the water table is so low that the shrubs get no moisture whatsoever from it and must live on what rain they get. The latter type of plants has developed all sorts of devices to slow down evaporation. The leaves may be small, or they may be covered with felty hairs, or they may have a varnished surface, or they may just drop off when hot weather comes to Death Valley.

Temperature and moisture—though they are vital—are not the only factors that control plant growth. Another important factor is the texture of the soil and its chemical content. Not even pickleweed will grow "in the rough" on the Devils Golf Course, for example. There is just too much salt for even that salt-tolerant plant to live.

One reason why botanists find Death Valley National Monument of especial interest is the occurrence of a few species that grow there and nowhere else. Others equally interesting are restricted to the Death Valley region, which includes the adjoining counties in California and adjacent Nevada. Those that grow in the monument and nowhere else are called endemics of that place. A few of the endemics are illustrated in this booklet. A few that are not pictured are: hollyleaf fourpodspurge *(Tetracoccus ilicifolius)*, napkinring eriogonum *(Eriogonum intrafractum)*, Gilman sandpaper-plant *(Petalonyx thurberi gilmanii)*, and Panamint lupine *(Lupinus magnificus)*. Some of the endemics are found only in limestone areas.

Trees are scarce in the monument except around the springs and the inhabited areas, though the mountain canyons and higher elevations have their quota. Athel tamarisk *(Tamarix aphylla)*, though it was originally an introduced tree, has made itself quite at home and can be found growing spontaneously around wells and springs on the valley floor. Cottonwood *(Populus fremontii)* grows naturally in some of the canyons of the higher ranges and it has also been planted as a shade tree. The date palm has been introduced and a fine orchard can be seen at Furnace Creek Ranch. A few of the other trees found in Death Valley are included in this booklet.

4

HOW TO USE THIS BOOKLET

In this booklet on Death Valley wildflowers we have attempted to make it easy for you to find the name of the plant that arouses your curiosity. Many more plants—be they shrubs, herbs, or even trees—that grow in the limits of the monument are not included here. We are limited by space, but we present to you those that you will see: because they are so common, or because they are so beautiful, or even some of those you will want to see because they are so interesting.

For those of you who are not botanists there are "clues" in conspicuous type at the bottom of the page which should help you spot your plant quickly. (Please remember you are in an area of the National Park System and DON'T PICK THE WILDFLOWERS.) Actually, just looking at the pictures will sometimes suffice. The first clue is habitat—the kind of place where the plant normally grows in Death Valley National Monument; the second is the type of plant—herb, shrub, or tree; the third is the color of the flower—or at least the predominant color. Flowers are often spotted, lined, or shaded with colors other than their predominant shade. They also may change from youth to age; for example, white evening-primroses fade to pink. It is obvious that there is no space within the three key characters at the bottom of each page to qualify "color" with its varying shades. The creamy yellow flowers of desert dandelion and the golden yellow ones of desertgold are both called yellow. No color is given for grasses, rushes, pines, and a few other plants.

Habitat is based on an informative discussion of California plant communities in *A California Flora* (pp 10-18) by Philip A. Munz. Habitat is the key character used to help you find the kind of places where the plants grow, but may also need qualifying remarks, as does color. Again, there is not space at the bottom of the page to make your key complete. Creosotebush, for example, is listed under "Valley floor and fans" where, in the monument, it is most abundant. You may see it, too, on the hot southern exposures of the "Upper desert slopes" or even occasionally on the gravel floors of the upper canyons (temperature is an important factor in the distribution of creosotebush). An explanation of what each habitat includes follows.

PLANT HABITATS

Valley Floor and Alluvial Fans. This includes the area from the valley floor to the foot of the steep slopes of the mountains. The

5

elevation is from below sea level to about 3,500 feet. Within this area are a few other distinctive habitats to which certain plants are restricted. In this case supplementary words are added; for example, Cooper rush would be listed as "Valley floor, marshes." These few supplementary subdivisions are defined below:

MARSHES—Mostly alkaline, and including springs, wells, ditches, and the surrounding drying meadows.

SALT FLATS—The floor of Death Valley is often called the "Chemical Desert." Along its edges will be found some salt-tolerant plants.

WASHES—These often extend above the line of alluvial fans into the lower slopes of the mountains.

LOWER CANYON WALLS AND CUT BANKS—A few plants grow in this habitat and are found nowhere else.

Upper Desert Slopes. This includes the densely shrub-covered slopes and broad valleys from approximately 3,500 to 6,000 feet elevation.

STREAM BEDS—May or may not have water showing at the surface.

CANYON WALLS—Some kinds of plants grow only on canyon walls. Some of these species live only in dry places. A few, such as Panamint phacelia and certain mosses, live only by wet seeps and dripping springs.

Pinyon-Juniper Woodlands. This is the area where the trees begin. Shrubs also are present. There is some overlapping of the preceding and following habitats. The juniper trees begin to appear at a lower elevation than the first pinyon pines. The area occupies approximately the 6,000 to 8,000 feet elevation.

SPRING AND CANYON WALLS

Limber-Bristlecone Pine Woodland. This area includes the scattered stands of pines and the open flats with low ground cover, some larger shrubs and occasionally cactus. This occupies the area between 8,000 and 11,000 feet.

PLANT NAMES AND PARTS

There are almost no botanical terms included in the "stories" about the plants in this booklet. You will need to know, however, that plants that are related are put into families: rose family, sun-flower family, and so forth. Within each family are more closely related groups called genera (singular, genus): for example, in the rose family, rose belongs to the genus *Rosa,* mountain-mahogany to the genus *Cercocarpus,* cliffrose to the genus *Cowania*—and there are about seventy more genera in the plant family in the world. Within each genus are species (singular, species); sometimes a few species, sometimes many and sometimes only one: for example, in the sunflower family, gravelghost (*Atrichoseris*)

6

has but one species, aster *(Aster)* has many species, rabbitbrush *(Chrysothamnus)* has several species. Occasionally there will be a third scientific name which is called a subspecies or variety; for example, the rubber rabbitbrush which is pictured within these covers has several names that are in this category. The scientific name for one of them would be written this way: *Chrysothamnus nauseosus mohavensis.* (In a scientific publication it would be more complete-even to the name of the botanists who described it *(Chrysothamnus nauseosus (Pallas)* Britton subsp. *mohavensis (Greene)* Hall & Clements).

The word fruit in the text may be somewhat confusing. It is used in the botanical sense, as an organ of the plant in which the seeds ripen. It may be dry or fleshy and may contain one seed or many, or may have several parts each containing seeds, like the fruit of desert fivespot.

Three plants in the list of illustrations do not have flowers and therefore no true seeds—two ferns and one puffball (a fungus). Other plants without true seeds have been reported within the limits of the monument. Several of them, as well as the ferns and fungi, are large enough to be noticed when walking about. For example, the scouring rushes or horsetails *(Equisetum)* and the selaginellas, which look like small dried-up plants in a rock garden, have been reported. Mosses must have moisture and are known to grow in canyons where conditions are favorable. The spots and other blemishes that are occasionally seen on stems and leaves give evidence of infestations of microscopic fungi. A detailed study of soil samples* shows the presence of both fungi and algae in the soil beneath desert shrubs and into the salt flat beyond the point where shrubs will grow. Perhaps the strangest group of plants are lichens. Strands of fungi and cells of green algae grow together and lose their own individual characteristics to form a composite structure that is the lichen plant body. These are many and varied and are classified into families, genera, and species as in other plant groups. Also as in other plant groups, descriptive words are commonly used to show their growth habits. Just as shrubby, leafy, and tree-like are often used with flowering plants so are lichens spoken of as crustose, squamulose, foliose, or fruticose. The last two types hopefully might be seen at higher elevations where more moisture and trees exist, but no list of Death Valley lichens seems to be available. A few genera of the other two categories have been reported and many of the crustose and squamulose lichens are associated with rocks so that some of the black, orange, or grey-green blotches that you see as you travel may be colonies of lichens in one or the other of these categories.

Plant Ecology of Death Valley, C. B. Hunt and L. W. Durrell; U. S. Geological Survey Professional Paper 509.

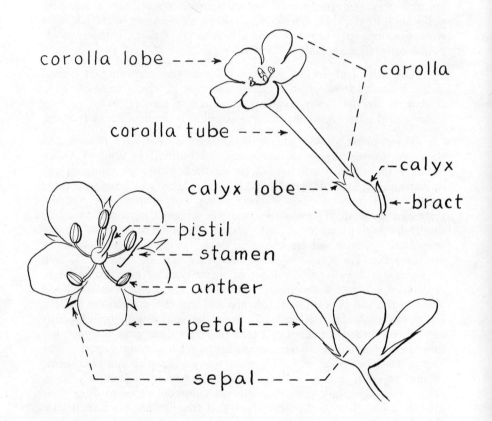

corolla lobe

corolla

corolla tube

calyx

calyx lobe

bract

pistil

stamen

anther

petal

sepal

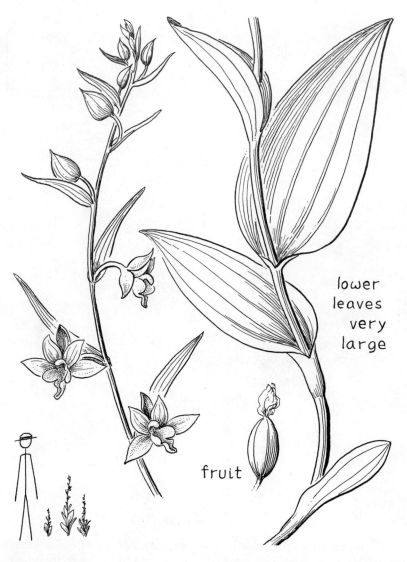

lower
leaves
very
large

fruit

STREAM ORCHIS   *Epipactis gigantea*   Orchid family

You might not expect to find orchids growing in Death Valley, but one is to be found in wet places in the upper canyons or on the valley floor. It grows to a height of one to three feet and is much more conspicuous for its large clasping leaves than its purplish flowers, which grow in the axils of the smaller upper leaves.

VALLEY FLOOR TO PINYON-JUNIPER WOODLAND, MARSH; HERB; PURPLE

9

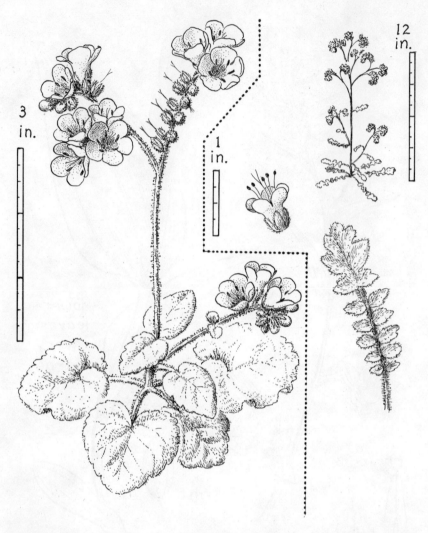

3 in.

1 in.

12 in.

CALTHALEAF PHACELIA   *Phacelia calthifolia*   Waterleaf family

The calthaleaf phacelia (above left) is a striking violet-flowered annual six to eighteen inches high with broad, dull greenish leaves. The whole plant is quite sticky and leaves a brownish stain on the hands which causes an irritating dermatitis on some people. Another violet-flowered phacelia *(Phacelia crenulata)*, the crenate phacelia (above right) is quite as common as the preceding but more widespread than calthaleaf phacelia throughout the desert regions. It, too, has ill-scented glandular foliage but the leaf blades are longer than wide and deeply lobed.

VALLEY FLOOR AND FANS; HERB; PURPLE

YELLOW TACKSTEM
PAGE 63

GOLDEN EVENING-PRIMROSE
PAGE 38

GOLDEN-EVENING PRIMROSE
PAGE 38

STANSBURY CLIFFROSE
PAGE 127

DESERT GOLDPOPPY
PAGE 33

DESERT GLOBEMALLOW
PAGE 28

MOHAVE DESERT-STAR
PAGE 65

SACRED DATURA
PAGE 62

DESERT MARIPOSA
PAGE 89

DEATH VALLEY MOHAVEA
PAGE 40

DESERT PRINCESPLUME
PAGE 90

EPIPACTIS
PAGE 9

TURTLEBACK
PAGE 44

FLAT-CROWN ERIGONUM
PAGE 51

TOBACCOWEED
(GRAVELGHOST)
PAGE 61

BIGELOW MIMULUS
PAGE 12

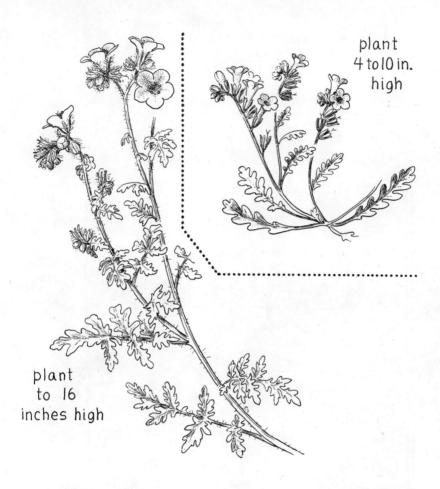

plant
4 to 10 in.
high

plant
to 16
inches high

Phacelias are represented in the west by many species and they grow in all sorts of places—sea coast, valleys, mountains, or deserts. The flowers are either white or various shades of purple, though some kinds are yellowish at the base. Several species, differing greatly in appearance, are found in Death Valley National Monument.

DEATH VALLEY PHACELIA *Phacelia vallis-mortae* Waterleaf family

Death Valley phacelia is a weak-stemmed annual growing up among desert shrubs. The leaves are much longer than they are wide and are parted into leaflets, the stem has bristly hairs, and the flowers are lavender. Though it was named for its presence in Death Valley, it is found as far east as southern Utah and south to northern Arizona. Fremont phacelia *(Phacelia fremontii),* on the upper right, branches at ground level. The flowers are yellow at the base. These phacelias grow on upper fans and also on upper desert slopes.

VALLEY FLOOR AND FANS; HERB; PURPLE

11

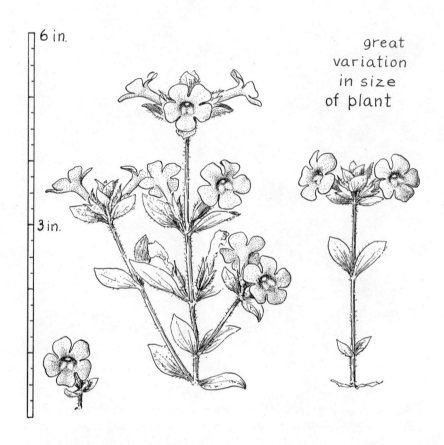

6 in.

great
variation
in size
of plant

3 in.

BIGELOW MIMULUS *Mimulus bigelovii* Figwort family

This is humorously classified as one of the "belly plants." The reason is obvious when one finds at one's feet in the sand or on the desert pavement a small bouquet of purplish red flowers with yellow centers that are spotted with purple. Flowers are not picked in a National Monument, so one gets down to its level for a better look. The flowers are large in relation to the plant and can be easily spotted as one travels around the deserts in early spring.

VALLEY FLOOR AND FANS; HERB; PURPLE

grows in
crevices
in-cliffs

Rock Mimulus *Mimulus rupicola* Figwort family

This mimulus is rarely seen. It has been found only a few times in some of the deep canyons surrounding the valley in the crevices of limestone cliffs. It is therefore one of the Death Valley endemics; this is another way of saying that it grows in Death Valley and nowhere else.

Valley floor and fans, Lower Canyon Walls; Herb; Purple

flowers have a
delicate, pleasing
fragrance

COOPER BROOMRAPE   *Orobanche cooperi*   Broomrape family

All the members of the broomrape family are root parasites without any green at all in the plants. In other words, they cannot manufacture their own food as the green plants do, but get theirs by attachment of their roots to those of other plants. Cooper broomrape seems to prefer white bur-sage (*Ambrosia dumosa*) as a host but "attachments" have been reported for other desert shrubs. The plants are six to twelve inches high and the larger ones occasionally branch. They are dark brown and rather dusty-looking. The flowers are deep purple, with a yellow mark in the throat, and they, too, have a grizzled look because of the very fine hairs on the outside of the corolla. The plant grows in the western deserts wherever its host may grow.

VALLEY FLOOR AND FANS; HERB; PURPLE

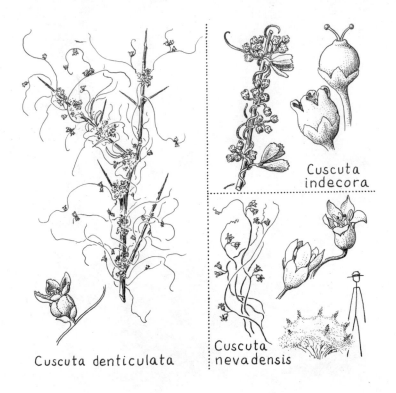

Cuscuta indecora

Cuscuta denticulata

Cuscuta nevadensis

DODDER *Cuscuta denticulata* Morning-glory family

At a distance this plant may look to you like handfulls of wet orange or yellow tissue paper that has been tossed away, now dried on the desert bushes. Examine it and one sees a tangle of yellow to brown leafless threads dotted with tiny clusters of whitish flowers or ripened pods. Dodder is a true parasite. After the small seedling vine leaves the ground and begins to twine on shrubs the microscopic wart-like suckers on its stem attach to a healthy stem of bur-sage, creosotebrush, or any of a dozen or more different hosts and the stage is set for more or less serious injury to the plant attacked. Dodder spreads as it acquires nourishment and the "threads" attach to other branches, each attachment making a completely new dodder plant that is soon at work destroying the host. No wonder it has been called "devil-gut" for its bad habits as well as "angel-hair" for its attractive golden threads.

There are three, perhaps four, species of dodder within the monument. Kinds of dodder are hard to tell apart. The flowers and fruits are small and delicate. The growth form is hardly helpful nor are the species consistent in choice of host. Enlargements of flowers of *C. denticulata* (left), *C. nevadensis* (lower right), and *C. indecora* (upper right) are given.

VALLEY FLOOR AND FANS; HERB

15

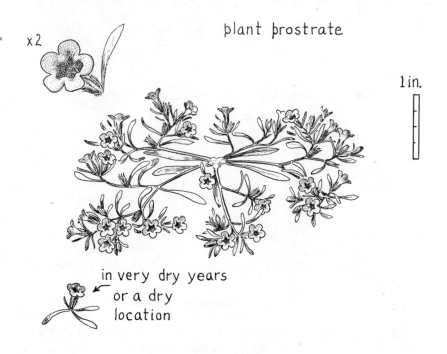

x2

plant prostrate

1in.

in very dry years
or a dry
location

NAMA (PURPLE-MAT) *Nama demissum* Waterleaf family

The slender stems of purple-mat spread out as much as ten inches in a green circle on the sand. Of course in drier years the plants have fewer branches and a much smaller spread. More than one variety grows in the Death Valley region, and another species as well, but both of them have the same habit of growth, and both are annuals. The narrow, tongue-shaped, hairy leaves (about one-half to an inch long) are more or less clustered at the tips of the stems and also at the base of the plants, and set among the leaves are the reddish purple, trumpet-shaped flowers. The flowers are about a half-inch long and are abundant on healthy plants. Where several flowering plants are growing near each other there is a fine splash of purple. Someone has said that purple-mat is just another pretty little "belly plant," but if you get to see it during its short life you will find it very rewarding.

VALLEY FLOOR AND FANS; HERB; MAGENTA

16

12 in.

ENGELMANN ECHINOCEREUS *Echinocereus engelmannii*
Cactus family

The cylindrical ribbed stems, loosely clustered and rather few, are liberally clothed with rather long spines of varying shades of red, yellow, white, brown, or gray. It has been called "calico cactus" because of the piebald appearance caused by the color variation which so often occurs in the spines. The flowers are usually pale magenta to purple. The ripe fruit is red and edible, the spines easily removed, the seeds tiny and black. Probably the original inhabitants of the valley as well as birds and rodents used the fruits as an addition to their diet. The plants occur as far south as northern Mexico.

fine hairs,
(no spines)

BEAVERTAIL PRICKLYPEAR *Opuntia basilaris* Cactus family

A clump of beavertail in full bloom is well worth a stop for a picture. You may think you are now seeing a cactus that is safe to touch, as it has no spines, but the small bunches of short hairs that dot the blue-green, sometimes wrinkled pads come off easily and are extremely irritating to the skin. The Panamint Indians are reported to have boiled the joints for food. The showy magenta flowers are borne on the margins of the pad-like joints.

VALLEY FLOOR AND FANS AND UPPER DESERT SLOPES; SHRUB; MAGENTA

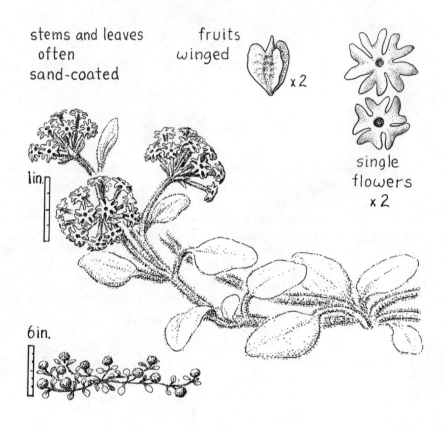

stems and leaves
often
sand-coated

fruits
winged

x2

single
flowers
x2

1in.

6in.

DESERT SANDVERBENA   *Abronia villosa*   Four-o'clock family

Perhaps this kind of sandverbena has been photographed for picture postcards more than any other desert wildflower. At least the low-growing plants with their heads of fragrant, rose-pink flowers have inspired many an amateur photographer. From a technical point of view the pretty verbena-like flower is not a corolla but a calyx brightly colored; nor is it a true verbena, though the flowers are of much the same shape. The hairs on the leaves are rather sticky and often are partially coated with sand. It is widespread in sandy places throughout the western deserts as far south as Sonora and Baja California, Mexico.

VALLEY FLOOR AND FANS; HERB; PINK

18

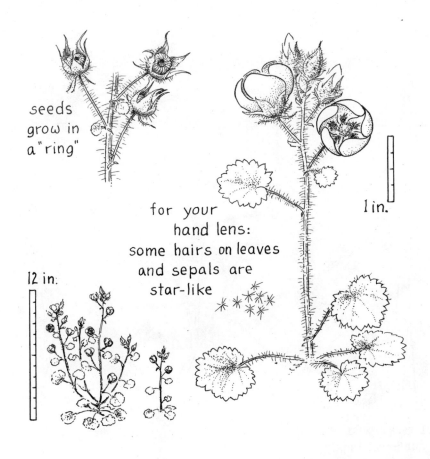

seeds
grow in
a "ring"

for your
hand lens:
some hairs on leaves
and sepals are
star-like

12 in.

1 in.

FALSEMALLOW (DESERT FIVESPOT) *Eremalche rotundifolia*
Mallow family

Judging by the number of common names, desert fivespot comes near to winning the popularity contest among the local wildflowers. It has been variously called lantern flower, Chinese lantern, fivespot mallow. The plants are usually less than a foot high, the leaves are round with a toothed margin, and though the plants have a conspicuous hairy covering they are green and not gray. The rose-pink petals of the flowers curve inward, thus suggesting a small lantern, but not enough to conceal the crimson spot at the base of each of the five petals. This plant will be seen on other deserts in the west, as it occurs as far south as northern Baja California, Mexico and in western Arizona. In some floras it is found under the generic name *Malvastrum*.

VALLEY FLOOR AND FANS; HERB; PINK

19

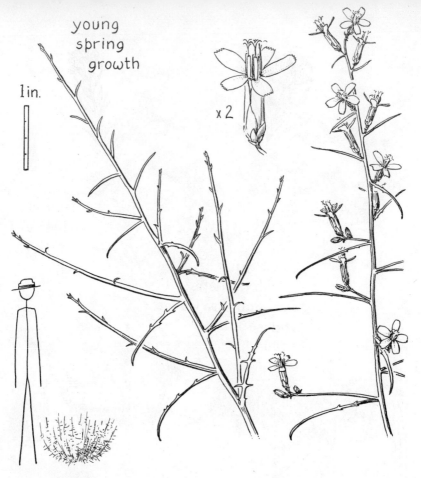

young
spring
growth

1 in.

x 2

DESERT WIRELETTUCE (DESERTSTRAW) *Stephanomeria pauciflora*
Sunflower family

Here at last is a plant in the sunflower family which has flowers
that are pink instead of some shade of yellow. This and other species
of the genus are quite common in southwestern deserts. The flowers
are small and few, and fade to a buff color. Most of the year wirelettuce is a tangled mass of dry, slender, straw-colored stems a foot
or so high which you will probably call just another kind of tumble-
weed. In early spring tender stems with milky juice come up from
the root and bear narrow, bluish green leaves with a few toothed
lobes on the margins. Desert bighorn eat many different kinds of
plants, but this in its spring stage is so attractive to them that they
will paw the young shoots out of the soil. They are bitter, but there
is no accounting for taste. Another kind of wirelettuce *(Stephanomeria parryi),* just a few inches high and bearing larger and more
abundant flowers, is found in the mountains at an elevation of 4,000
or 5,000 feet.

VALLEY FLOOR AND FANS; SHRUBBY HERB; PINK

20

leaves
silvery-
silky

ARROWWEED PLUCHEA *Tessaria sericea* Sunflower family

In some floras arrowweed is assigned to the genus *Pluchea.* Arrowweed, here and elsewhere in the west, is never far from water, though the water may be underground quite a few feet. It is more tolerant of alkaline conditions than the mesquite, which also likes an underground water supply. One sees the willow-like growth of arrowweed throughout the valley around springs and wells and the alkaline marshes and meadows that surround them, and on the broad expanse of valley floor under which water drains from the upper part of the valley to below sea level. Like pickleweed and mesquite, arrowweed is often partially buried in drifting sand. At the southern end of the sand dunes there is a strange assemblage of plants known as the Devils Corn Field. The "shocks" form when soil is blown from around the plants and is caught and held in their roots and branches. Arrowweed was not used for arrow shafts according to Coville's report on plants used by the Panamint Indians, but other tribes have used the straight stems for that purpose.

VALLEY FLOOR AND FANS, MARSHES; SHRUB; PINK

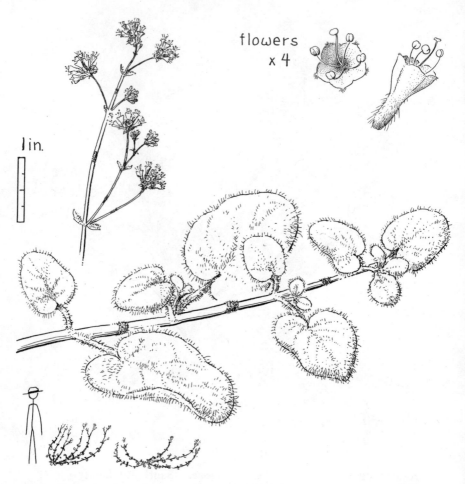

flowers
x 4

1 in.

Wetleaf spiderling *Boerhaavia annulata* Four-o'clock family

On the floor of the valley and the alluvial fans one sees bunches of large, bright green leaves quite different in appearance from the usual desert plants. Frederick Coville, who made the first collection in 1891 on the Death Valley Expedition, said that before the flowering stems grew up, it looked like a begonia plant. The small lavender flowers, which blossom from March to May, are not as conspicuous as the leaves. The underside of the leaf is wet to the touch, a fact that explains the common name. Sticky reddish brown rings occur on the coarse stems between the few stem-leaves and often trap small insects. At one time wetleaf was thought to grow only in Death Valley but has since been found in other desert valleys in the region. Another kind with larger flowers grows in southern Nevada and Utah.

Valley floor and fans, washes; Herb; Lavender

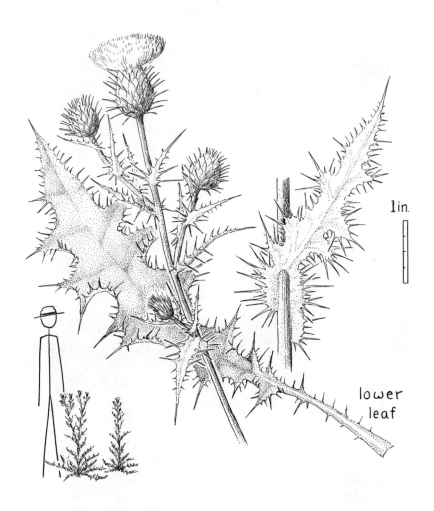

1 in.

lower
leaf

MOJAVE THISTLE   *Cirsium mohavense*   Sunflower family

The plants of the Mojave thistle grow to a height of about three feet. The stems and leaves are white with a cobwebby covering. The flower heads are lavender to pink and, including the spiny bracts that surround the mass of pink florets, about an inch and a half long. Mojave thistle has been found only in the California deserts. Probably it may also occur in adjacent Nevada. It always grows where water is or has been and can tolerate a great deal of alkalinity in the soil. The rugged desert bighorn seem to enjoy the thistles, thorns and all. Those around the marshy springs where the sheep come for water are always imperfect specimens because of their browsing.

VALLEY FLOOR AND FANS, MARSHES; HERB; LAVENDER

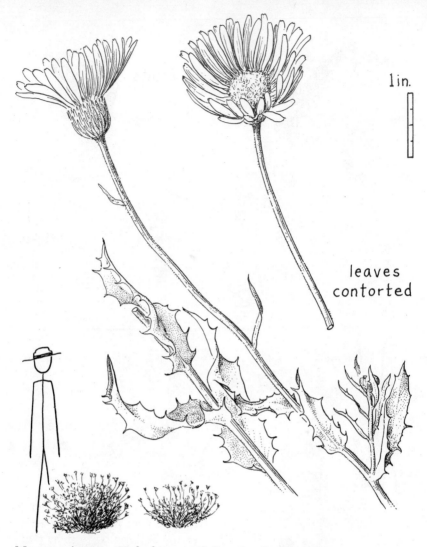

1 in.

leaves
contorted

MOJAVE ASTER *Xylorhiza tortifolia* Sunflower family

    According to some botanists the name of this little shrub might still be *Machaeranthera tortifolia or Aster abatus,* which are names it bears in some of the less recent floras. This is an instance where continuing studies by botanists have resulted in a group of species being re-assigned from one genus to another, to better reflect plant relationships. The flower color of Mojave aster is lavender—quite different from the usual bold colors of most desert wildflowers. The flowers are large, however, and abundant in season, so they are readily seen. The foliage is grayish and the leaves spiny-toothed. The plants are quite common in nonalkaline soil and grow all over the western deserts from California to the Mexican border and east to southern Utah.

VALLEY FLOOR AND FANS AND UPPER DESERT SLOPES;
SHRUB; LAVENDER

24

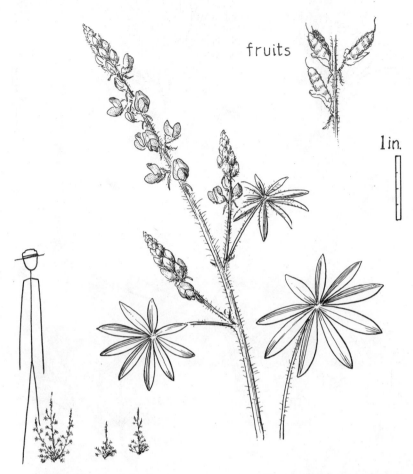

fruits

1 in.

The species of lupines are not as well represented in Death Valley National Monument as in wetter or cooler places in the west. Several kinds occur, however, some on the valley floor, others with the limber and bristlecone pines, and still others in the cool damp upper canyons.

ARIZONA LUPINE *Lupinus arizonicus* Pea family

Arizona lupine, which is widespread elsewhere in the west, is commonly found in sand and gravel at low elevations in Death Valley. It is a leafy-stemmed annual up to three feet high but usually much less. The flowers, though plentiful, are not crowded. They are light blue, often having shades of pink. The oblong pods are nearly an inch long. This is closely related to another species, *Lupinus sparsiflorus.*

VALLEY FLOOR AND FANS; HERB; BLUE

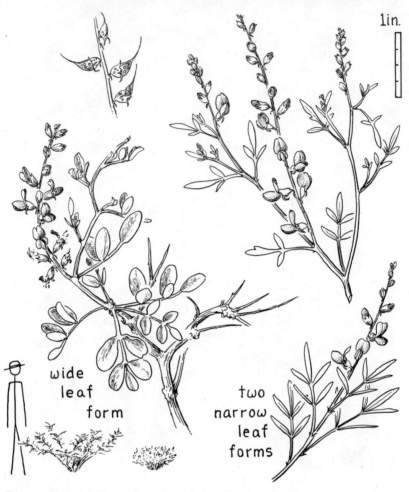

1in.

wide
leaf
form

two
narrow
leaf
forms

Indigo Bush *Psorothamnus fremontii* Pea family

Two forms of this "desert beauty," as the shrub is sometimes called, occur in the monument. Both are equally beautiful. They are difficult to tell apart and part of the difference lies in the width of the leaflets and the pubescence that covers them. Many spikes (two to three inches long) of small, royal blue, pea-shaped flowers rise above the gray leaves. The bushes are much branched and from one to about three feet high. Those of the upper alluvial fans are conspicuous also in their leafless state. The stems and branches are white and their form is that of a broad-crowned oak tree in miniature. The roundish sharp-pointed pods are dotted with brown glands. Indigo bush with its varieties is widely distributed in the southern part of the Great Basin and in the deserts southward. It is sometimes treated as a species of the genus *Dalea*.

Valley floor and fans; Shrub; Blue

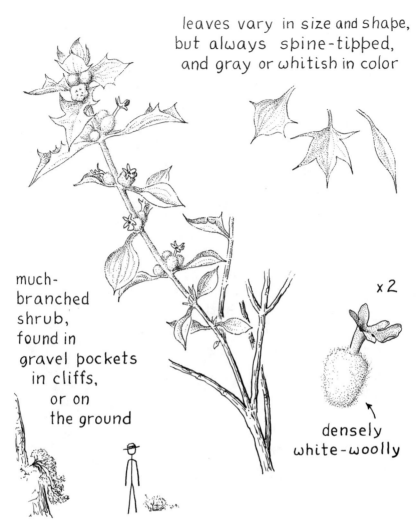

leaves vary in size and shape,
but always spine-tipped,
and gray or whitish in color

much-
branched
shrub,
found in
gravel pockets
in cliffs,
or on
the ground

x 2

densely
white-woolly

DEATH VALLEY SAGE   *Salvia funerea*   Mint family

Death Valley sage is often a straggly shrub two feet or so in height with bright blue or violet-blue flowers which are in clusters in the leaf axils. The flowers themselves are partially embedded in white wool. The young branches and the leaves are white with a covering of very short hair, and the leaves have marginal spines, though these are often reduced to one only at the leaf tip. Death Valley sage grows at low elevations at the bases of canyon walls or in the side gullies draining into the canyons or may hang from cliffs. So far as is known, Death Valley sage is found only in the canyons draining into Death Valley and can be considered to be a true endemic.

VALLEY FLOOR AND FANS, CANYON WALLS; SHRUB; BLUE

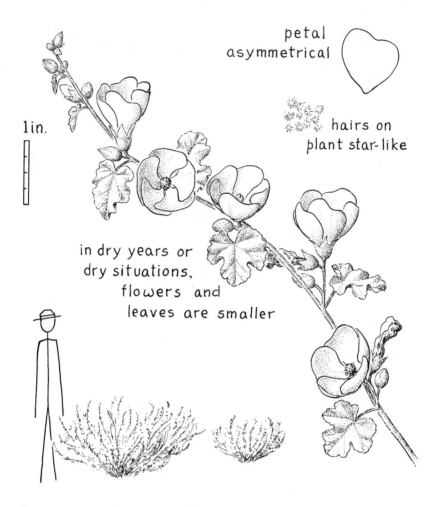

petal asymmetrical

1 in.

hairs on plant star-like

in dry years or dry situations, flowers and leaves are smaller

DESERT GLOBEMALLOW   *Sphaeralcea ambigua*   Mallow family

The woody portion of this plant is mostly limited to the crown and lower branches, while the upper stems and branches are, as a rule, many and pliable. The leaves are an inch or two long, rather broad, and usually three-lobed, and the star-shaped hairs cover them as thickly as they do the other parts of the plant. The flowers are a shade of red not too often seen among the desert wildflowers. It has been designated as "grenadine" but to some it is more nearly the color of a piece of fresh salmon. The species is widespread in the southwest and is highly variable. There is a form of Rusby globe-mallow *(Sphaeralcea rusbyi eremicola)* that is an endemic of Death Valley.

VALLEY FLOOR AND UPPER DESERT SLOPES; SHRUB; RED

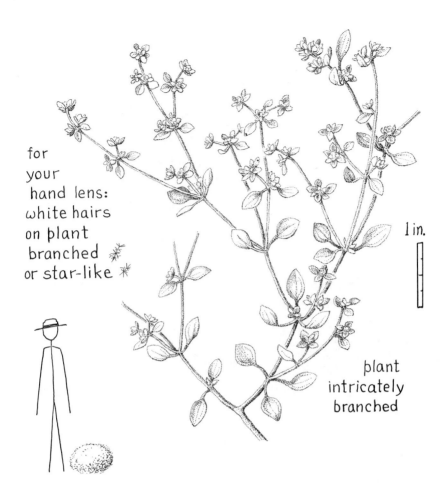

for
your
hand lens:
white hairs
on plant
branched
or star-like

1 in.

plant
intricately
branched

HONEYSWEET TIDESTROMIA   *Tidestromia oblongifolia*
Amaranth family

This is a plant that thrives under really difficult conditions. These rounded gray-green perennial herbs are found with desert-holly saltbush at the lower edge of the creosotebush scrub where it meets the alkali sink of the salt pan area. In fact it *will* grow on the salt flats to some extent. The foot-high plants, broader even than high, are conspicuous more because of the complete lack of other plants in these hot bare places than from their own attractiveness. The flowers are tiny and clustered in the axils of the leaves. They deserve their common name because they are fragrant. That fragrance, though, is mostly wasted on the desert air as the flowers normally bloom in late summer when few visitors are in the area.

VALLEY FLOOR AND FANS; SHRUBBY HERB; YELLOW

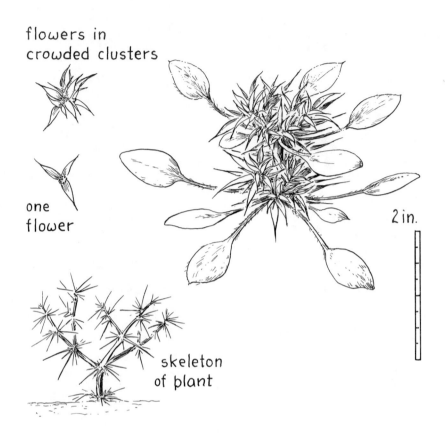

flowers in
crowded clusters

one
flower

2 in.

skeleton
of plant

SPINY CHORIZANTHE   *Chorizanthe rigida*   Buckwheat family

Here is a plant that can be identified by its "skeleton." This can
be done with several other annuals you see in the fall and winter
months when only the dead stalks remain of the spring and summer blooming. Spiny chorizanthe, as you see it on the gravelly or
rocky flats, is more conspicuous dead than alive for the spiny
bracts that surround the flowers become extremely rigid and darker,
and the short stem (one to three inches long) takes on a woody
texture. In life its most conspicuous feature is the woolly leaves,
which have stalks much longer than the leaves themselves. The
tiny greenish yellow flowers are so concealed by the spiny bracts
that a hand lens is needed to examine them. The plants are rather
common throughout the western deserts.

VALLEY FLOOR AND FANS; HERB; YELLOW

plants yellow-green
in flower; brighter
yellow all over
when fruits
ripen

flowers x 4

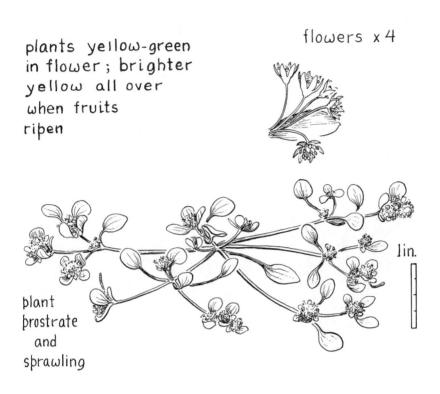

plant
prostrate
and
sprawling

1 in.

DEATH VALLEY GILMANIA (GOLDCARPET)   *Gilmania luteola*
Buckwheat family

A botanist's delight is this small prostrate plant with small
yellow-green leaves and yellow flowers. It is very rarely seen, except
in the best years, and grows only on the lower parts of some of the
washes in Death Valley and nowhere else. Plants such as this that
are restricted locally are known as "endemics." When this plant
was first described as new by Frederick Coville, it had a different
scientific name. Due to certain rules concerned with the naming of
plants, another generic name must now be used. Fortunately, the
new name honors another botanist who contributed much to the
knowledge of the flora of Death Valley, M. French Gilman.

VALLEY FLOOR AND FANS; HERB; YELLOW

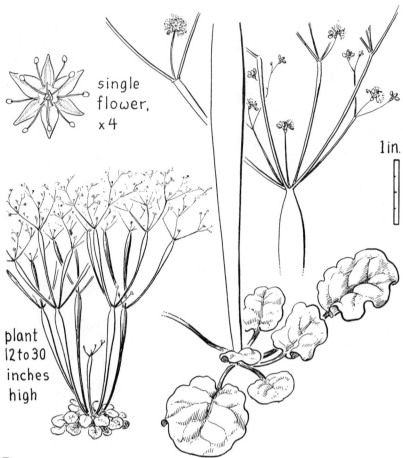

single flower, x 4

1 in.

plant 12 to 30 inches high

DESERT-TRUMPET ERIOGONUM *Eriogonum inflatum*
Buckwheat family

This eriogonum can be easily identified by its distinctive shape, a growth form which occurs to some degree in a few other species. The main blue-green hollow stem of desert-trumpet arises from the basal cluster of leaves, slender below and swelling above to a diameter of about one-half of an inch. From this summit, several branches spread out and they in turn become little "trumpets" and branch again into the slender branchlets that bear the small clusters of tiny yellow flowers. Even late in the season the dead trumpet-shaped stalks are easy to spot as one drives along the roads on the floor of the valley. It is a variable species in its wide range over the southwestern deserts, and the most marked variation is known by the scientific name of *Eriogonum inflatum deflatum*. You can doubtless figure out from the name what *that* looks like.

VALLEY FLOOR AND FANS; HERB; YELLOW

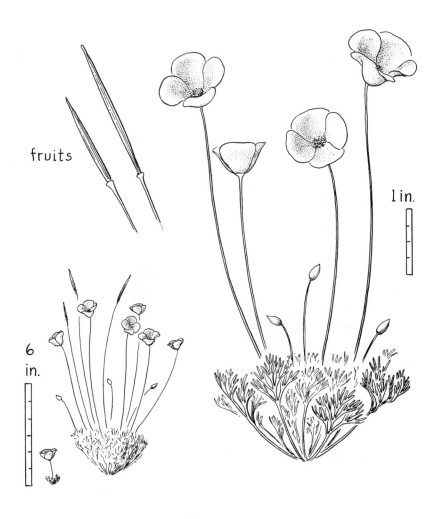

fruits

1 in.

6 in.

DESERT GOLDPOPPY *Eschscholzia glyptosperma* Poppy family

This small relative of the California state flower grows usually to a height of two to ten inches. The flowers are about an inch across, each one borne at the top of a leafless stalk which rises well above the clustered blue-green divided leaves at the base of the plant. Though small the plants are often very showy as they have many flower-bearing stems. This annual poppy grows in sand or on the desert pavement and is often seen while one is traveling on the roads in the monument.

VALLEY FLOOR AND FANS; HERB; YELLOW

33

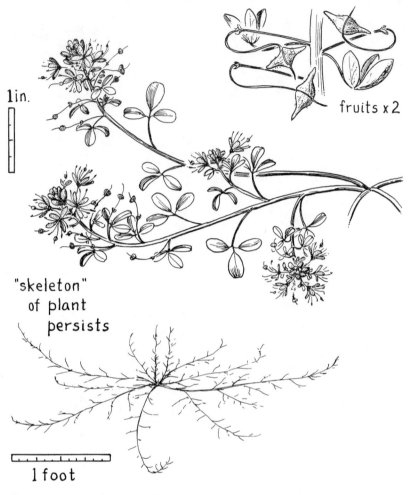

1 in.

fruits x 2

"skeleton"
of plant
persists

1 foot

BUSHY CLEOMELLA   (STINKWEED)   *Cleomella obtusifolia*
Caper family

Stinkweed is not unattractive in spite of the unpleasant odor
of the yellow-green foliage. The plants may be small (five to ten
inches high) or the sprawling stems may spread about two feet.
The flowers are yellow and the small leaves resemble clover leaves.
The stalked capsule (dry fruit) has an angular shape, the angles
often drawn out laterally into a pair of horns. The fruits are about
the size of the pickled capers one finds on the fancy groceries shelf,
and the ripe seeds are reported to be much enjoyed by doves. It is
common all over the Mojave Desert area and adjacent Nevada
and Arizona, mostly growing in loose alkaline loam.

VALLEY FLOOR AND FANS; HERB; YELLOW

34

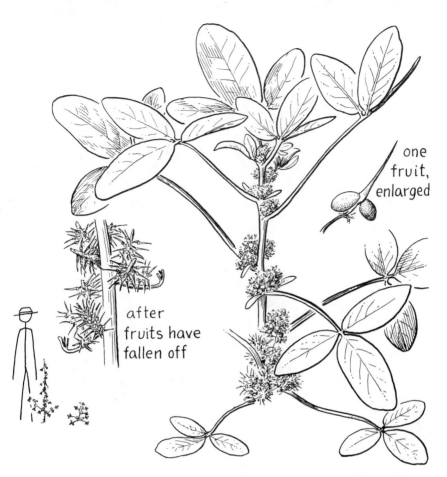

one fruit, enlarged

after fruits have fallen off

FALSE-CLOVER (SPINY CAPER) *Oxystylis lutea* Caper family

On April 28, 1844, John C. Fremont was returning along the Old Spanish Trail to the east from one of his expeditions. The party stopped at a stream called the Amargosa, "bitter water of the desert," where he saw a patch of yellow-green herbs which he thought belonged to the mustard family. The plants that he pressed and took home with him were described as a new genus and species, *Oxystylis lutea*. You will find the same kind of herb growing on the floor of the valley and in like areas to the eastward in saline places where the underground water is at a high enough level to supply its needs. The erect plants grow from a few inches to three feet in height; the leaves are in threes; the flowers are small and yellow and grow in clusters close to the stem; the fruits have a single sharp spine and the fruit clusters look like burrs along the stem and remain until the stout dead stalks blow away in the desert wind.

VALLEY FLOOR AND FANS, MARSHES; HERB; YELLOW

35

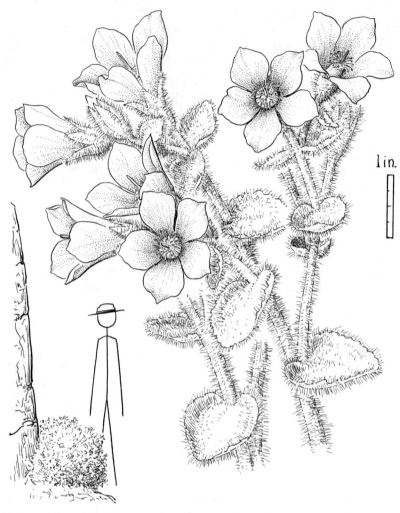

1 in.

STINGBUSH (DESERT ROCKNETTLE) *Eucnide urens* Loasa family

The stingbush is a handsome perennial to look at but definitely not a plant to touch because of the long sharp barbed bristles and the hairs which can be very irritating. In spite of this, the hardy desert bighorn enjoy browsing on it. This rather brittle shrub grows to a height of two feet and is even broader than it is high. It is found at the bases of canyon cliffs or the cut banks of the alluvial gravel at the mouths of the canyons and—but more rarely—on the fans. The leaves are broad, an inch or more long. The large flowers are pale yellow with a greenish tinge and appear in spring. It grows in similar places southward through the deserts.

VALLEY FLOOR AND FANS, CANYONS; HERB; YELLOW

36

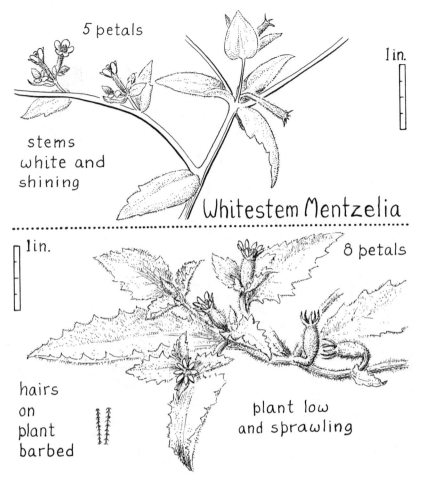

5 petals

1 in.

stems
white and
shining

Whitestem Mentzelia

1 in.

8 petals

hairs
on
plant
barbed

plant low
and sprawling

DEATH VALLEY MENTZELIA *Mentzelia reflexa* Loasa family

Though the Death Valley mentzelia is not as showy as one of the other mentzelias *(Mentzelia tricuspis)* which occur occasionally here, it is especially interesting, as it was long thought to grow only in the Death Valley region. It has more recently been found in central San Bernardino County. The plants are short and spreading and very leafy. The yellow petals and many stamens are conspicuous among the leaves, and when the seeds are ripe the stalk of the capsule is sharply turned downward. The leaves are covered with tiny barbed hairs that stick to anything they touch, hence the name "stick-leaf" has been sometimes used as a name for the whole group. The other kinds that grow in the region also have this clinging character. One of the small-flowered kinds, whitestem mentzelia *(Mentzelia albicaulis)* is illustrated at the top of the page.

VALLEY FLOOR AND FANS; HERB; YELLOW

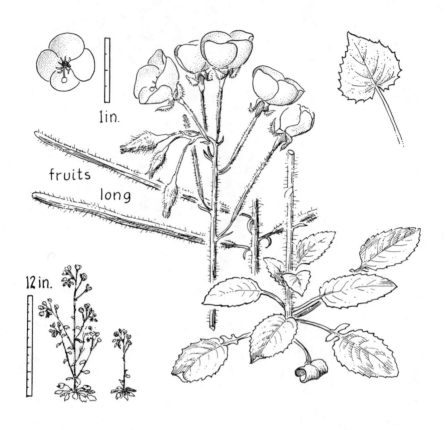

fruits
long

1 in.

12 in.

GOLDEN EVENING-PRIMROSE *Camissonia brevipes*
Evening-primrose family

From February through April from sea level to 4,000 feet this bright yellow evening-primrose may be seen someplace in travels around the monument. It may be found in the open desert among the black stones of the desert pavement or in sand in the washes, and it sometimes grows in stands thick enough to give color to the alluvial fans. The individual plants are often well over a foot high. The flowers, several on a stalk, are an inch or more across, and the ripening long narrow capsules spread almost at right angles. The leaves are mostly at the base and are attractive, too, with their toothed margins and reddish veins. The desert bighorn seem to enjoy it for early spring greens. It is common in the deserts of California and those of the states nearby. The flowers of a form of the heartleaf evening-primrose, *(C. cardiophylla),* a plant which grows in washes at the foot of canyon walls, much resemble this. The toothed heart-shaped leaves (upper right) help to distinguish it from the preceding.

VALLEY FLOOR AND FANS; HERB; YELLOW

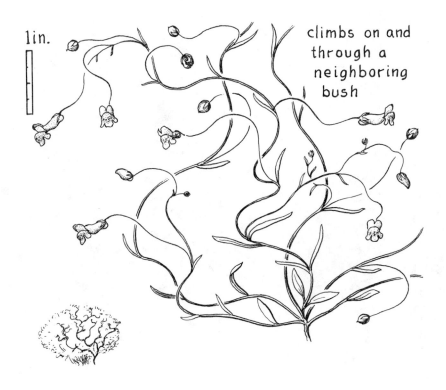

1 in.

climbs on and
through a
neighboring
bush

YELLOW TWINING SNAPDRAGON *Antirrhinum filipes*
Figwort family

Like many of the desert annuals that are delicate and fragile, twining snapdragon gets its initial protection and additional moisture by starting its short life at the base of some desert shrub. The shrub then becomes the necessary support for this tangled green-stemmed plant with its scattered narrow leaves. The yellow flowers, which are about an inch long, are borne at the ends of the tendril-like branches. Yellow twining snapdragon grows in loose sandy soil in both California deserts and in desert places as far east as Arizona and southern Utah. In the *Illustrated Flora of the Pacific States* this species is to be found under the genus *Asarina*.

VALLEY FLOOR AND FANS; HERB; YELLOW

3
in.

DEATH VALLEY MOHAVEA *Mohavea breviflora* Figwort family

This annual is quite commonly seen in the early spring growing in sand or gravel—later, sometimes, if rains are favorable. Though not as showy as its larger-flowered southern relative, *Mohavea confertiflora*, the short sticky-leaved plants are rather attractive with their yellow flowers which remind one of snapdragons. They are short-lived, however, and when the thin-walled capsules soon break and spill out the many black seeds, they look very different but still rouse your curiosity. This species grows in southern Nevada and northwestern Arizona as well as the Death Valley region.

VALLEY FLOOR AND FANS; HERB; YELLOW

40

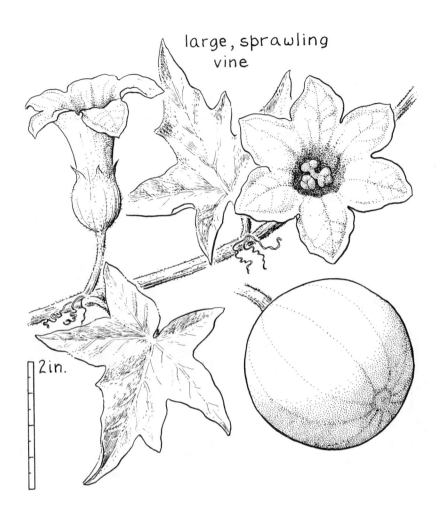

large, sprawling vine

2 in.

PALMLEAF GOURD (COYOTE MELON) *Cucurbita palmata*
Gourd family

Occasionally in the washes you will see a familiar-looking vine with large yellow flowers and palmately lobed leaves trailing over the sand and gravel. Too many members of the gourd family—cucumbers, watermelons, squashes, for instance—are well known in the home vegetable garden for you not to recognize the familiar shape of the blossoms. Supposedly the gourds are edible; and possibly the Panamint Indians used the seeds at least, but better leave both for the desert rodents. The broken gourds give evidence that it has, for them, food value. This species grows in the California, Nevada and Arizona deserts.

VALLEY FLOOR AND FANS, WASHES; HERB; YELLOW

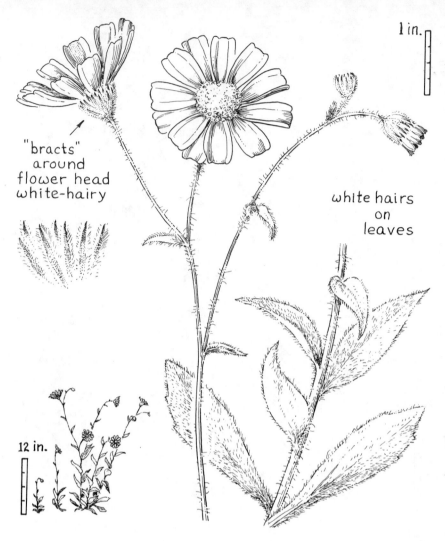

"bracts" around flower head white-hairy

white hairs on leaves

1 in.

12 in.

DESERTGOLD *Geraea canescens* Sunflower family

Even in years when there is not much rainfall, this showy sunflower can be found in the first spring blooming on rock-covered flats or in sandy places above the low white alkaline stretches of the valley. It grows rather commonly throughout the deserts of the southwest. The desert sunflower is an annual six inches to two feet tall with a rather harsh feel to the stems and leaves and fuzzy white bracts at the base of the attractive fragrant yellow-flowered heads, which are much visited by insects. Because the plants occur so commonly, the seeds serve as a dependable crop for small rodents to harvest for food. Many other common names have been used for this widespread desert species.

VALLEY FLOOR AND FANS; HERB; YELLOW

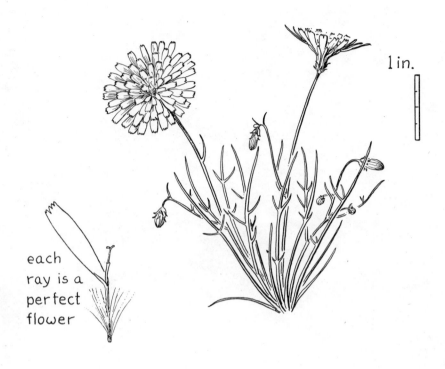

each
ray is a
perfect
flower

1 in.

DESERT DANDELION (DESERT MALACOTHRIX)
Malacothrix glabrata Sunflower family

Of the plant families that grow in Death Valley, the sunflower family is represented by the greatest number of different kinds of plants. This is hardly surprising, however, when it is remembered that the sunflower family is the largest one among the flowering plants, and that representatives of it grow all over the world from the tropics to arctic regions. Desert dandelion grows in sandy places in the Great Basin region southward through the deserts to northern Mexico. This annual is quite conspicuous in good years. The pale yellow flower heads contrast with the lush, dark green, finely divided leaves. As usual, it is quite a different story in the all-too-frequent dry years. Then the small plants can support only two or three flower heads.

VALLEY FLOOR AND FANS, WASHES; HERB; YELLOW

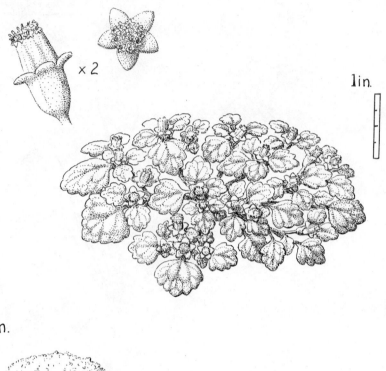

1in.

6 in.

TURTLEBACK   *Psathyrotes ramosissima*   Sunflower family

There are few common names among the wildflowers that are as descriptive as "turtleback" is for this gray-leaved member of the sunflower family. Along the roadsides, and in other places if you care to walk, you will see rounded mounds of leaves growing from a woody root, just about the size and shape of a desert tortoise shell. As the size of a desert herb is always dependent on the water it receives, in some years your "turtles" may be small indeed. The flower heads are yellow; the leaves are thickish and wrinkled and give off an odor much like turpentine; the plants will grow in loose sand or gravel or the more compacted soils of the desert pavement. Turtleback is a native of the western desert regions.

VALLEY FLOOR AND FANS; HERB; YELLOW

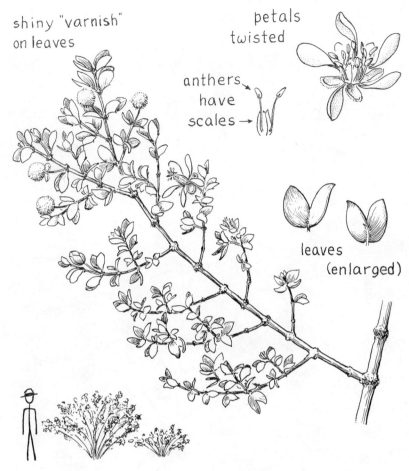

shiny "varnish" on leaves

petals twisted

anthers have scales →

leaves (enlarged)

CREOSOTEBUSH   *Larrea tridentata*   Caltrop family

This is perhaps the most common shrub of the deserts of the west at elevations below the Joshua trees and the pinyon pines. It is not to be expected, however, on alkali sinks and the salt pans. After the rains which may occur in its flowering periods, the creosotebush has the appearance of a well-kept garden shrub. The grayish stems with their blackish joints then have an abundance of dark green leaves, and the branchlets bear the conspicuous bright yellow flowers. The small fuzzy white fruits that develop later show up nicely against the evergreen foliage. The odor given off by the creosotebush is highly controversial. Some find it extremely disagreeable, while others think it interesting and pleasant. After a rain the odor is intensified and one would know even in the dark that there were creosotebushes about.

VALLEY FLOOR AND FANS; SHRUB; YELLOW

45

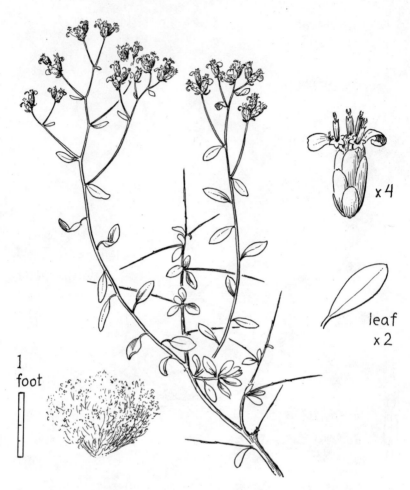

x4

leaf
x2

1
foot

AMPHIPAPPUS (CHAFF-BUSH) *Amphipappus fremontii*
Sunflower family

This, as well as the many other plants of the sunflower family included in this booklet, has yellow flowers. The shrubs are not more than a foot in height but are often much wider, as the slender whitish branches and branchlets curve outward and then upward from the main axils. The oblong leaves, which are one-half an inch or less long, are scattered, and the small flowering heads are clustered at the tips of the many branchlets. The whole aspect of the plant is yellow-green. Amphipappus grows in rocky canyons or alluvial fans or rocky mesas, often to an elevation of 5,000 feet. It can be found in similar places in the desert areas of California, northern Arizona, and southern Nevada east to southwestern Utah.

VALLEY FLOOR AND FANS UPPER DESERT SLOPES; SHRUB; YELLOW

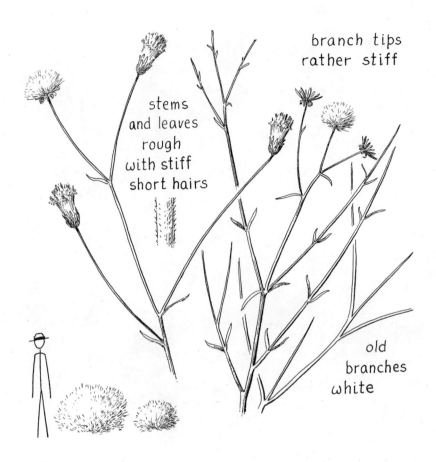

branch tips
rather stiff

stems
and leaves
rough
with stiff
short hairs

old
branches
white

SWEETBUSH BEBBIA (SWEETBUSH) *Bebbia juncea aspera*
Sunflower family

This is far from being one of the more beautiful shrubs of the area, but it is often seen in trips around the valley. The rounded dense masses of small green, usually leafless twigs, which are rough to the touch, grow sometimes to a height and breadth of three feet or more. The fragrant flower heads, which have no petal-like rays, are orange-yellow and scattered all over the outer twigs. They appear almost anytime that moisture and temperature are favorable for them. At least the chuckwallas like this shrub, as one of the common names that has been given to it implies, and the desert bighorn find it an excellent browse plant. It is not restricted to this part of the country and is found as far south as Baja California, Mexico.

VALLEY FLOOR AND FANS; SHRUB; YELLOW

SPRUCEBUSH (PIGMY CEDAR)   *Peucephyllum schottii*
Sunflower family

Whether it is called sprucebush or pigmy cedar this shrub has a good descriptive name, as the dark but vivid green needle-like leaves are reminiscent of conifers. Even in a half-dead state after a long stretch of drought, the branches that are still alive are conspicuously leafy. The shrubs (three to six feet high) are shaped like small juniper trees. The yellow flower heads are apt to appear after the winter rains. Pigmy cedar is common in the broad washes in the ranges and occasionally even grows on the canyon walls. It was first collected by Arthur Schott along the Colorado River during the Mexican Boundary Survey in the early 1850's. The species name of this widespread plant was given in his honor.

VALLEY FLOOR AND FANS, WASHES; SHRUB; YELLOW

WESTERN HONEY MESQUITE *Prosopis glandulosa torreyana*
Pea family

Honey mesquite is a friend of man and beast. Perhaps it is not
the friend to man that it was in the days when the Panamint Indians,
and Indians elsewhere, harvested the nutritious pods and ground
them into food. Now man at least can use its wood for campfires
and its shade to protect him from the sun, excepting those mesquites
that have ceased to be trees because their trunks and branches are
buried in the sand dunes. Throughout its wide range the pods and
foliage are eaten by cattle; bees and other insects use the greenish
yellow flower spikes. Mesquite is a deciduous tree about fifteen or
twenty feet tall and much branched, and on the smaller branchlets
there are cruelly strong spines. The screwbean mesquite *(Prosopis
pubescens)*, which has the woody pods tightly coiled, also grows
in Death Valley.

VALLEY FLOOR AND FANS, SALT FLATS AND MARSHES;
TREE; YELLOW

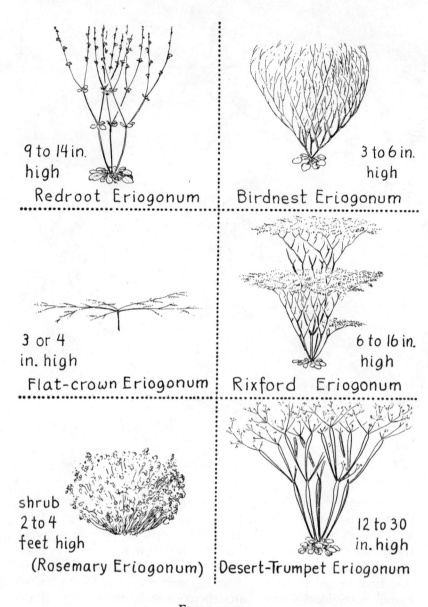

9 to 14 in. high
Redroot Eriogonum

3 to 6 in. high
Birdnest Eriogonum

3 or 4 in. high
Flat-crown Eriogonum

6 to 16 in. high
Rixford   Eriogonum

shrub 2 to 4 feet high
(Rosemary Eriogonum)

12 to 30 in. high
Desert-Trumpet Eriogonum

Eriogonum

There are more kinds of eriogonums growing in Death Valley National Monument than of any other genus of plant, though in number of species the evening-primrose and gilia are close rivals. Among the many kinds, there is much variety in shape or form of the plant itself; in flower color, which may be white, shades of pink, yellow, or even red; in places where the different species grow, which may be from below sea level to the top of Telescope Peak.

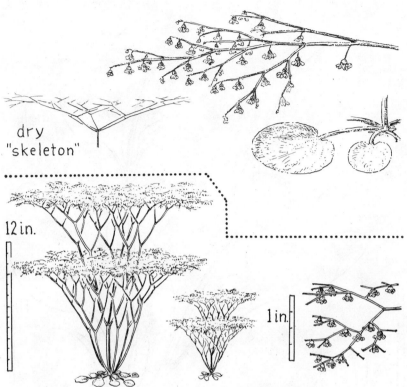

dry
"skeleton"

12 in.

1 in.

FLAT-CROWN ERIOGONUM *Eriogonum bachypodum*
Buckwheat family

In summer in the disturbed soil along the roadsides and in the run-off stream beds in the alluvial fans, one sees many plants of the annual flat-crown eriogonum and other kinds that are related to it. If you have seen in movies those flat-topped trees so characteristic of the African veldt, you will find the same shape repeated in this desert plant which is only a few inches high and normally well over a foot broad with all the branches in one plane. The small white flowers are clustered in glandular involucres which are attached to the underside of the branches. The most striking of the related kinds is the Rixford eriogonum *(Eriogonum rixfordii)*. In this (lower drawing), the plants may be six inches to a foot or more in height, depending upon how much water it has had that season. The round basal leaves and the flowers are much the same as those of the flat-crown erigonum. The branches, however, are not in one plane but several and rise in stories like a pagoda. This species, unlike the preceding which ranges far southward, is limited to Death Valley and the area adjacent to it.

VALLEY FLOOR AND FANS; HERB; WHITE

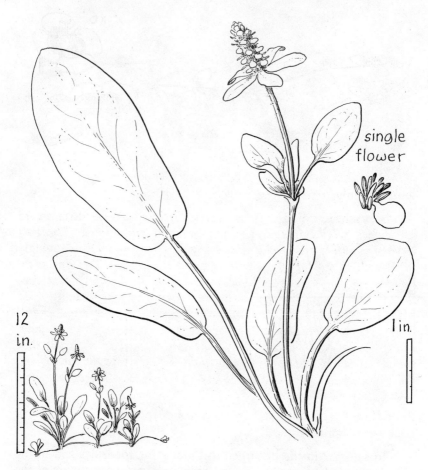

single
flower

12
in.

1 in.

YERBA MANSA   *Anemopsis californica*   Lizards-tail family

Yerba mansa is the only native representative of the lizards-tail family in the west, but it is widespread and grows as far east as Colorado and Texas and south into Mexico. It always grows near water, and in Death Valley it is commonly seen around seeps and springs. There it forms mats that are made by its creeping stems or runners, which root and form new plants in the same manner as the common strawberry. The large oblong leaves are attractive, but its chief attractions are the flowers. What you think is one flower is really many. Each inconspicuous flower is set above a tiny white bract and arranged in spikes, and what appear to be petals are large white bracts set below the spike. It is much like an anemone in appearance, and its scientific name means anemone-like. The plants are aromatic, and the root is peppery in taste. Supposedly the whole plant has some medicinal virtue.

VALLEY FLOOR AND FANS, MARSHES; HERB; WHITE

52

WHITEMARGIN EUPHORBIA   *Euphorbia albomarginata*
Spurge family

In washes and in smaller watercourses there are mats six to ten inches wide flattened against the sand and gravel. The tiny leaves are bluish green and glabrous and are covered with seemingly white-petaled flowers that nestle among the leaves. The tiny male flowers and the single female flower are set in a small green cup. This in turn is rimmed by dark maroon glands to which are fastened white petal-like appendages, thus making the best imitation "flower" known (except of course for the plants of the sunflower family, where the individual flowers or florets are clustered into heads that appear to be distinct flowers, such as daisies, dandelions, sunflowers, and many others). This and the following species are sometimes referred to the genus *Chamaesyce.*

dry
skeleton"

PARISH EUPHORBIA   *Euphorbia parishii*   Spurge family

Though not as attractive as the preceding species, Parish euphorbia is more conspicuous. It grows where plants are few and widely spaced in alkaline soils and its tangled flattened reddish stems are bare most of the year. It is primarily a prostrate plant like the preceding but often is set up an inch or so above the ground on its woody root because the wind blows the soil away from its base. The tangled branches are inclined to turn up at the tips as if they could not endure the terrifically high temperatures of the ground level. The leaves are smaller than white-margin euphorbia and the "flowers" have no white appendages.

VALLEY FLOOR AND FANS, WASHES; HERB; WHITE

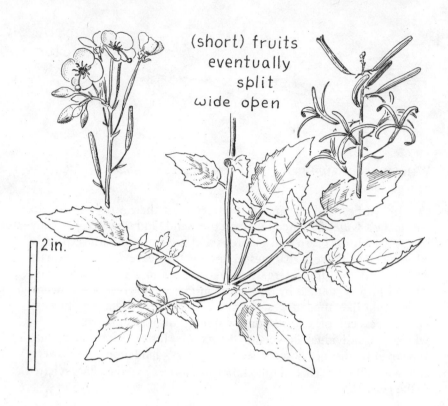

(short) fruits
eventually
split
wide open

2 in.

BROWN-EYED EVENING-PRIMROSE *Camissonia claviformis*
Evening-primrose family

When you buy a seed packet of annual larkspur to plant in your garden you expect to get white or pink flowered plants as well as blue—and maybe ones with other minor differences—from the seeds of this one species. This seems normal to you in cultivated garden plants, but you may be surprised that, in some groups at least, this sort of thing goes on all the time in nature. This is very true of the evening-primrose pictured here. All over our western deserts named forms of this species occur; ones with green or grayish leaves, or ones with flowers without a dark spot on each petal and with colors that range through white, cream, buff, and pale yellow. Death Valley has at least two of these variants. This plant has the growth habit of the golden evening-primrose but is shorter than that plant usually is, and the flowers are smaller. The stalked capsules are about an inch long, narrow and blunt at the top. This is one of the most abundant flowering plants to be found on the valley floor.

VALLEY FLOOR AND FANS; HERB; WHITE

woody
skeleton
_of_
plant

2
in.

SHREDDING EVENING-PRIMROSE   *Camassonia boothii condensata*
Evening-primrose family

The woody skeleton of this desert annual will remain for more than one season unless it is dragged away by some desert rodent for home-building purposes. The stems of the flowering plants are stout, and as they age the loose papery bark of the stems comes off. The white flowers, which become pinkish as they wither, are densely set along the stem and have a definitely one-sided appearance as the stems lengthen. The smaller plants may be unbranched, but more often one sees plants with a few curved branches raising from the base. The bases of the narrow capsules are woody and remain on the spreading dead branches. There are several other species of evening-primrose with small to tiny flowers found within the monument, but they are much more slender and fragile in appearance than this one. All have the typical four-petal-ed, slightly cupped flowers and ball-shaped stigma which are character-istic of this genus.

VALLEY FLOOR AND FANS; HERB; WHITE

55

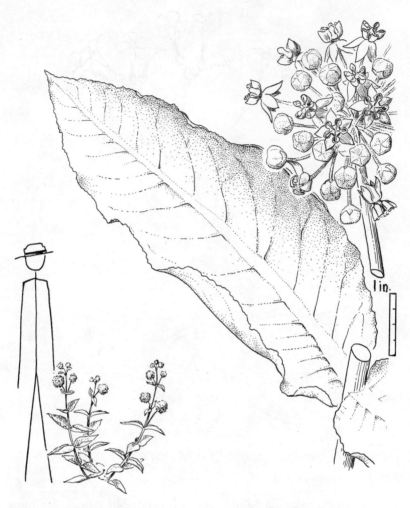

1 in.

DESERT MILKWEED   *Asclepias erosa*   Milkweed family

The tall dead stalks (two to four feet or more) of the desert milkweed remain standing after the leaves, flowers and fruits have blown away with the desert wind. The plants grow in the loose soil of the washes and, at least in the desert, never occur in large stands but as scattered groups of plants. The large leaves are broad, whitish green, rather thick in texture, and grow opposite each other, fitting closely against the stem. The whole plant appears to be covered with a loose white lint which rubs off as the plant grows older. The flower clusters grow from the axils of the upper leaves. The species is widespread in western desert regions and is found occasionally on the seaward side of the mountain ranges.

VALLEY FLOOR AND FANS, WASHES; HERB; WHITE

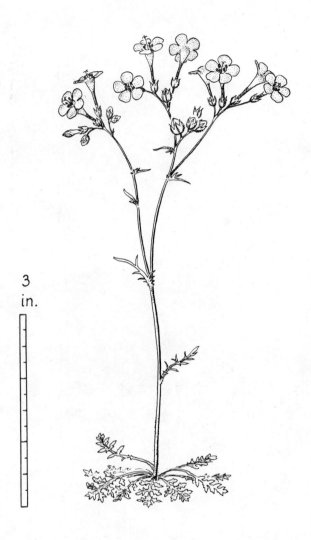

3
in.

BROAD-FLOWERED GILIA *Gilia cana triceps* Phlox family

In the flowers of the phlox family in general all colors of the rainbow can be found, though the white-violet-blue series is more common. The flowers of the broad-flower gilia have more than their share of color: the lobes are pink-lilac, the throat is blue on the upper part and yellow below, and the tube is deep purple. In addition to this, the stamens, which are to be seen in the top of the throat, are blue. In good years the plants grow to a foot or so in height and the several flowers are nicely displayed on the leafless branching stem.

VALLEY FLOOR AND FANS

for your
hand lens,

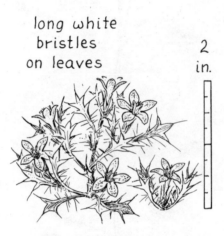

single
petal

long white
bristles
on leaves

2
in.

SPOTTED LANGLOISIA (LILAC SUNBONNET) *Langloisia punctata*
Phlox family

Get down on your knees for a good look at this plant which is only one to three inches tall. It is quite noticeable, though, for it is a perfect bouquet of five-lobed white (or lilac-tinted) flowers spotted with dark purple, and each lobe has in addition a central line. The leaves, which are large for a plant so small, are three-toothed at the tip and furnished with a few long white bristles on the margin. It grows in the **Mojave** Desert east to Arizona and Nevada.

VALLEY FLOOR AND FANS AND UPPER DESERT SLOPES; HERB; WHITE

58

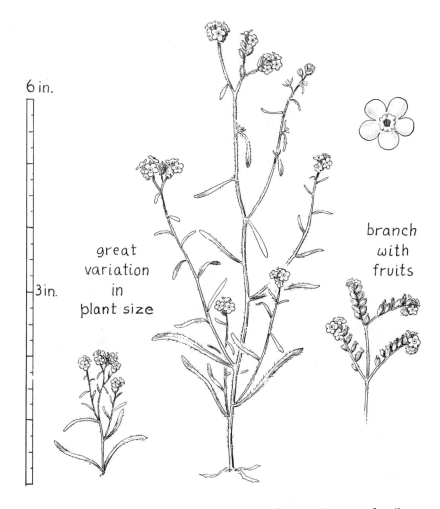

6 in.

great
variation
in
plant size

3 in.

branch
with
fruits

SCENTED CRYPTANTHA *Cryptantha utahensis* Borage family

There are several species of *Cryptantha* in various places in the monument and all are rather small annual plants with white flowers which are very tiny to small. The flowers of many of them are half concealed in stiff spreading hairs. The hairs around the flowers of the scented cryptantha are smoothly pressed flat and give a silky appearance to the inflorescence. The flowers have the odor of heliotrope. The plants are usually six to ten inches high and are commonly found at elevations of from 2,000 to 3,500 feet. They are seldom sufficiently abundant to give color at flowering time to the area in which they grow. They are found growing in similar places as far east as southern Utah.

VALLEY FLOOR AND FANS; HERB; WHITE

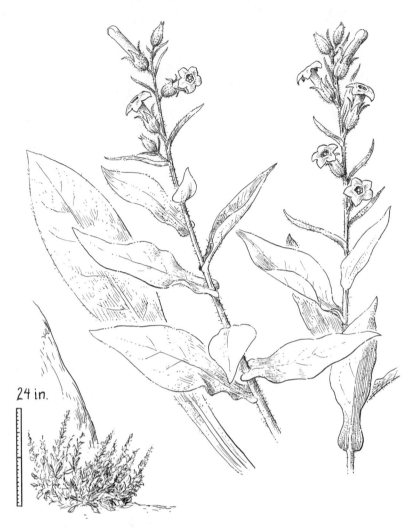

24 in.

DESERT TOBACCO   *Nicotiana trigonophylla*   Potato family

The herbage of this ill-smelling sticky member of the potato family is more conspicuous than its tubular, greenish white flowers which grow among the shorter leaves on the tops of the stems of this sprawling many-stemmed plant. The natural habitat here as well as elsewhere in the southwestern deserts is at the bases of cliffs and banks of canyons and washes. If you see it in other places it will undoubtedly be in the shade of some big boulder on an alluvial fan. Even in the driest season the dull, dark green leaves catch the eye. Other kinds of wild tobacco in the west have been used by various Indian tribes for smoking and probably this one was smoked by the local tribes in the Death Valley region.

VALLEY FLOOR AND FANS, LOWER CANYON WALLS; HERB; WHITE

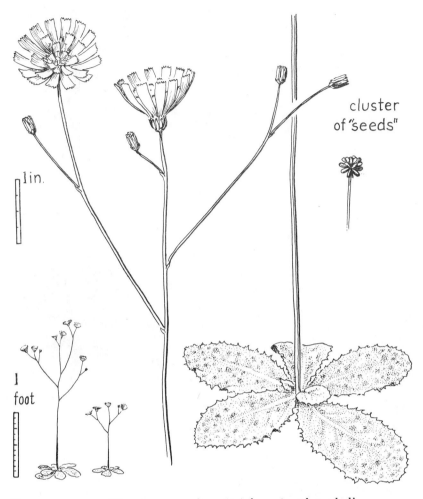

cluster of "seeds"

1in.

1 foot

TOBACCOWEED (GRAVELGHOST) *Atrichoseris platyphylla*
Sunflower family

There is only one species or kind of gravelghost, and it grows
on low washes and rocky slopes all over the western deserts. The
broad bluish brown-spotted leaves make flat rosettes on the ground
which blend with the sand and gravel, and the leafless stems rise
from them to the height of one foot to two and one-half feet. The
white or purplish-tinged, fragrant flower heads are borne on the
upper part of the stem. They are about one inch across and make
an attractive sight from February to May (or later if the rains come
late) waving in the desert wind. If you are far enough away, the
flowers on the slender stems seem to float in the air—and so the
name "gravelghost" has been given to it.

VALLEY FLOOR AND FANS, WASHES; HERB; WHITE

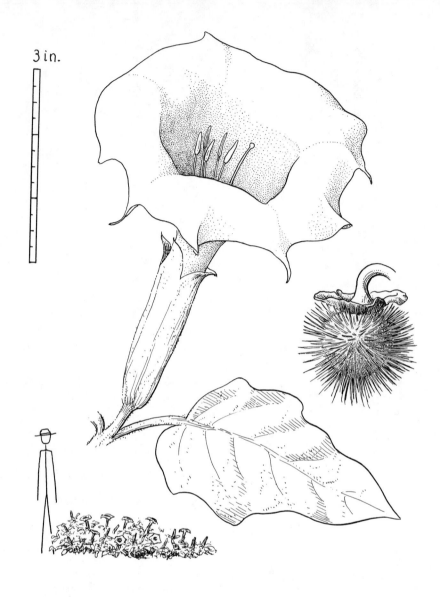

3 in.

SACRED DATURA   *Datura meteloides*   Potato family

This large herb grows in canyon washes but is never common. The herbage is grayish green and ill-smelling. The abundant flowers are as large as Easter lilies and fragrant. It grows from Mexico northward and its occurrence here may have been encouraged by early Indian tribes who used the plant in religious rites to induce visions.

VALLEY FLOOR, FANS AND ABOVE, WASHES; HERB; WHITE

12 in.

WHITE TACKSTEM   *Calycoseris wrightii*   Sunflower family

In the chicory tribe of the sunflower family the flower heads, which look like ordinary flowers, are made up of many strap-shaped florets. The dandelion in your lawn is an excellent example of this type. Several members of this tribe occur in Death Valley: desert dandelion *(Malacothrix glabrata)*, desert wirelettuce *(Stephanomeria pauciflora)*, New Mexican rafinesquia *(Rafinesquia neomexicana)*, and others. One of the others is white tackstem, which can be seen quite often growing in loose sandy soil. The flower heads of this annual are white with the back of the rays brushed with pink. The leaves are much divided and the "tacks" which give the plant its common name are the pale stalked glands on the upper stem. There is another species *(Calycoseris parryi)* with yellow flower heads and darker tack-shaped glands. Both kinds occur in southwestern deserts.

VALLEY FLOOR AND FANS; HERB; WHITE

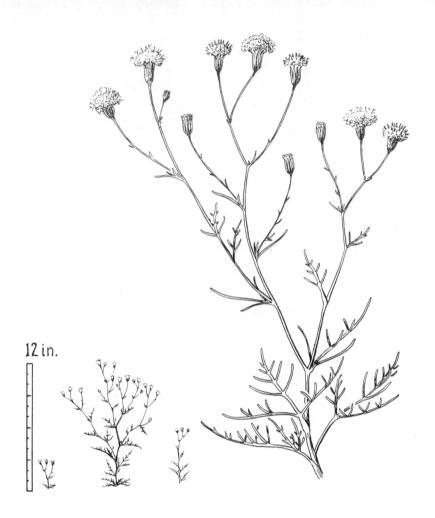

12 in.

PEBBLE   CHAENACTIS (PEBBLE PINCUSHION)
Chaenactis carphoclinia   Sunflower family

Several kinds of chaenactis grow in this area. One kind is found on Telescope Peak, others in various lower habitats down to the pebble chaenactis, which seems to prefer one of the hottest spots of all in the valley—the desert pavement. It grows from here eastward and southward, to Utah, western Arizona and northern Mexico. As it is an annual it has a short life span. The water supply its short roots can reach soon evaporates in the desert heat and it dies. Its height and the number of branches from the main axis, of course, depend on the water supply. If it is a year of several winter rains the plants may be over a foot high, with several stems from the base, and bear many white flower heads over which the stamens stand up like little pins. In dry years the plants are puny and can support only a few flower heads.

VALLEY FLOOR AND FANS; HERB; WHITE

64

white, stiff hairs
on stems and leaves

1in.

facetiously called
a "belly flower"

one bends low
to see them

Mojave desert-star *Monoptilon bellioides* Sunflower family

Desert star is another annual of the area that well deserves
to be called a "belly plant." The branches with their scattered, dull
green, hairy leaves flatten in the gravel in a circle three to six inches
wide. The flowers look much like daisies—those pleasant little
weeds of our lawns—in size and color. They cling as closely to the
soil as do the stems and leaves. A close-up color shot of desert star
is well worth the time spent in taking it.

Valley floor and fans; Herb; White

65

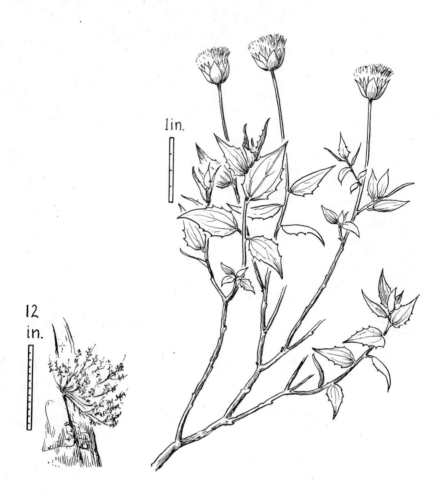

1 in.

12 in.

SPEARLEAVED BRICKELLIA   *Brickellia arguta*
Sunflower family

Some plants that grow on canyon walls may grow in other habitats as well but this one, to grow at all, must have its roots buried in cracks and crevices of the rocks here in Death Valley or in other southwest desert ranges. Perhaps it needs the additional shade that it will get some part of the day on the cliffs of the canyon. The plant grows in loose clumps. The flower heads are few and creamy white, but the leaves are its most interesting feature. These are an inch or less long, very firm and rather shiny, and sharply toothed around the margin.

VALLEY FLOOR AND FANS, CANYON WALLS; SHRUB; WHITE

CALTHALEAF PHACELIA
PAGE 10

LEWIS FLAX
PAGE 120

ROCKLADY MAURANDYA
PAGE 94

DODDER
PAGE 15

DESERT PUFFBALL
PAGE 67

DESERT INDIAN PAINTBRUSH
PAGE 88

BEAVERTAIL PRICKLYPEAR
PAGE 17
DESERT FIVESPOT
PAGE 19

MOHAVE ASTER
PAGE 24

LILAC SUNBONNET
PAGE 58

PANAMINT DAISY
PAGE 95

STANSBURY PHLOX
PAGE 117

DESERTGOLD
PAGE 42

DESERT DANDELION
PAGE 43

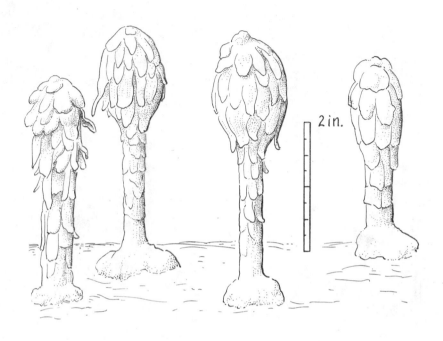

2 in.

DESERT PUFFBALL   *Podaxis pistillaris*   Puffball family

Driving along the roads, you may catch sight of a few gleam-
ing white objects in the compacted silty soil on alluvial fans and
valley floor, or even pushing through the blacktop of the roads.
You will doubtless stop, expecting to pick up something that has
been tossed out of a passing car, and find, instead of a bit of refuse,
a mushroom. Desert puffball is bright white, grows sometimes to
a height of six inches, and has an egg-shaped scaly top to the stalk.
Do not feel inspired to use this in cooking, for it is very dry. It is
not at all the kind of mushroom that you are accustomed to see
in the woods but is a kind of puffball instead, one which someone
has aptly described as a "puffball on a stick."

VALLEY FLOOR AND FANS; FUNGUS; WHITE

old plant looks like
bunch of white fluff

1in.

FLUFFGRASS   *Erioneuron pulchellum*   Grass family

This small bunchgrass will be noticed more in age than in youth. As it is commonly found growing among the blackened rocks of the desert pavement, the ripened fluffy grains and the thin straw-colored bracts that surround them make this tufted grass very conspicuous even though it is only a few inches high. In the monument there is another bunchgrass *(Blepharidachne kingii)* which might be confused with fluffgrass. It, too, is short and has hairy fruits, but the stems that bear the fruits are longer than the basal leaves. Fluffgrass can reproduce new plants from the old ones in an interesting fashion. The leaf-bearing branches arch over to the ground, root at the leaf cluster, and you have a new plant started. *Blepharidachne* reproduces new plants from seeds only.

VALLEY FLOOR AND FANS; HERB

68

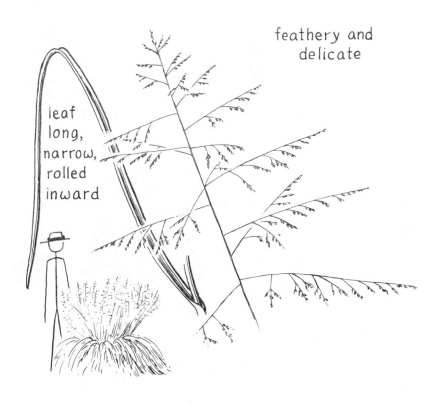

feathery and delicate

leaf long, narrow, rolled inward

ALKALI SACATON (DROPSEED)   *Sporobolus airoides*
Grass family

Alkali sacaton, which can be up to three feet in height, grows in large tough bunches. The stems that bear the flowers are slender and at least one-half the height of the whole plant. When the tiny fruits are ripe, the stems are much branched and very open and delicate-looking. The plants grow in more or less alkaline meadows with saltgrass and various sedges. It is a good forage plant; hence one may not be so fortunate as to see it in its feathery beauty because it has been grazed. Ancient Indian storage barrows were often lined with it.

VALLEY FLOOR AND FANS, MARSHES; HERB

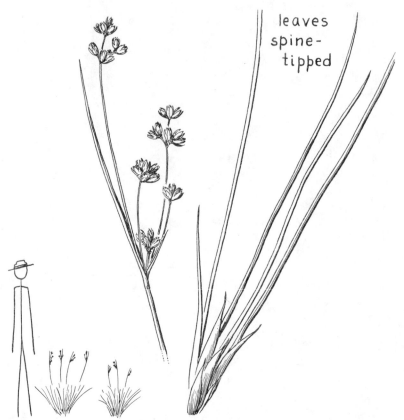

leaves
spine-
tipped

COOPER RUSH   *Juncus cooperi*   Rush family

Many kinds of marsh plants grow around the springs, seeps, and wells of the valley floor and fans. The soil is pale gray or white with bleached-out minerals. Here and in no other habitat in the valley you find bulrushes and other members of the sedge family, and with them sacaton, saltgrass, yerba mansa, California satintail, screwbean mesquite, blue-eyed grass, thistle; also genera like goldenrod, loosestrife, epipactis, baccharis, arrowweed, and others which, though they need water, do not always demand so much alkalinity. Cooper rush is at home in these surroundings, here and in similar places in the southwestern deserts. It grows in large tufts one and one-half to nearly three feet high, and the round stems are stiff and pointed. The clusters of flowers are inserted below the sharp-pointed tip of the stem. The flower parts are dry and straw-colored and look the same when fresh as they do around the ripe capsule. Rushes are one of the several plants the Indians traditionally used in basket-making.

VALLEY FLOOR AND FANS, MARSHES; HERB

stem
cross-
section
triangular

BULRUSH *Scirpus americanus* Sedge family

Bulrush, in Death Valley at least, is one of that assemblage of plants associated with the alkaline marshes and meadows around wells and springs. However, it has to have its roots in surface water. Coville remarks upon it in the "Botany of the Death Valley Expedition." The plants growing so closely packed together always indicated the soft muck underneath. The Expedition found so frequently that their horses mired almost disastrously in the clumps of it that short cuts through that type of marsh were never taken. Bulrush often grows to a height of more than four feet. The triangular stem is distinctive of this plant. The species grows from the coast to the desert. In fact, it is one of the common sedges of North· America. Some botanists interpret the Death Valley populations as belonging to the species *Scirpus olneyi.*

VALLEY FLOOR AND FANS, MARSHES; HERB

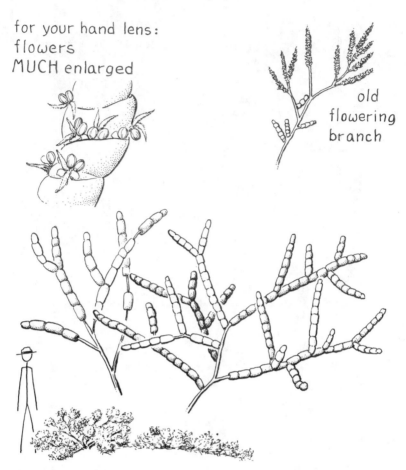

for your hand lens:
flowers
MUCH enlarged

old
flowering
branch

PICKLEWEED (IODINEBUSH) *Allenrolfea occidentalis*
Goosefoot family

Pickleweed is really a small shrub though often its woody stems are completely buried in drifting sand, much in the same manner in which the mesquite trees appear to be shrubs when buried in the sand dunes. It is most selective in the type of soil in which it will grow, and it will be found in strongly alkaline places in Death Valley and in similar situations throughout its wide range in the west. As you leave the Devils Golf Course or Salt Creek the dark blue-green masses of vegetation catch the eye. If you stop and look at the pickleweed you will think that it has no flowers or leaves. It has, but they are so tiny and modified that you need a good hand lens to examine them. The stems are fleshy and green, and the joints are short. It makes one think of tiny green sausages strung along a slender twig.

VALLEY FLOOR, ALKALI FLATS; SHRUB

72

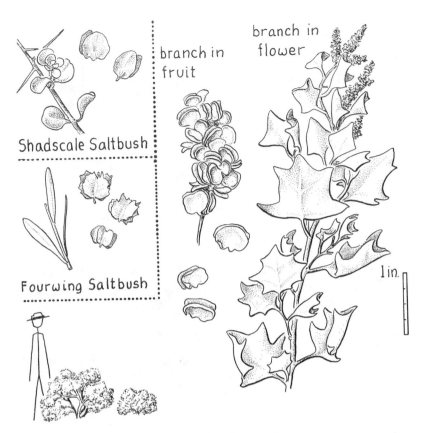

branch in fruit

branch in flower

Shadscale Saltbush

Fourwing Saltbush

1 in.

DESERTHOLLY SALTBUSH   *Atriplex hymenelytra*
Goosefoot family

Excepting creosotebush, desertholly is perhaps the best-known shrub in the monument. It is not uncommon throughout the southwestern deserts. In the growing season the toothed leaves (about one inch long and almost as wide) are white, strongly flushed with green. In the hot season the leaves are white, sometimes with a rosy tinge, as are also the round-winged fruits. The male and female flowers are on different plants. It is more tolerant of alkali than creosotebush and will even grow on the edge of the salt flats, but it is more commonly found growing in washes or alluvial fans to an elevation of 2,000 or 3,000 feet. Several other species of saltbush occur throughout the monument, and the fruits and leaves of two of them are illustrated. Shadscale saltbush *(A. confertifolia)*, a grayish white shrub with spiny branches, is usually found on alluvial fans and lower slopes of mountains, while fourwing saltbush *(A. canescens)* is commonly found in more well-watered areas on the valley floor.

VALLEY FLOOR AND FANS; SHRUB

HOPSAGE   *Grayia spinosa*   Goosefoot family

Hopsage is readily identified among its other gray-green associates—winterfat, bud sagebrush, blackbush, shadscale, and others—that grow on the upper desert slopes and flats. It is also found at lower places in the gravel beds of both the wide and narrow washes that cut through the alluvial fans. These washes tend to be the meeting-place of shrubby plants of upper desert slopes and the valley floor.

The bushes are 1-½ to 4 feet high and branch widely. The branches taper in age to a spiny point, not as painful to meet up with as the very stiff spinescent branches of spiny menodora or black brush (*Coleogyne*). The narrow leaves are about an inch long. The inconspicuous male and female flowers which come along in spring are on separate plants or merely separate branches. This may be the time of year when it earns its reputation as a fairly good browse plant, but what catches the eye of the traveler comes later with the ripening seeds. Each seed is enclosed in 2 rounded, papery, pink or white bracts which are crowded together on the branchlet tips and quite visible to the passerby.

UPPER DESERT SLOPES AND FLATS; SHRUB

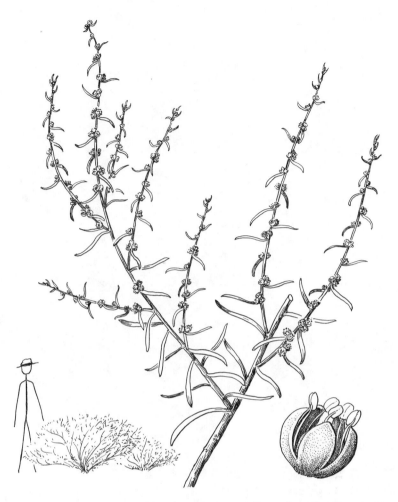

INKWEED (SEEPWEED)   *Suaeda torreyana*   Goosefoot family

Inkweed is not as salt-tolerant as pickleweed nor has it the same mound-forming habit. Consequently it grows farther from the saltpan edge. Usually it is found in intermediate positions between the saltgrass (*Distichlis*) meadows and its shrubs and the foot of the fans where moisture is even less accessible. It can be spotted by its dark bluish-green foliage which contrasts sharply with all of its neighbors except pickleweed. Inkweed is 2-3 feet tall and about equally wide from its woody base. The slender leafy branches spread at angles; the narrow leaves nearly an inch long are not crowded; and the tiny flowers are crowded in the leaf axils. Western Indians elsewhere have used foliage and seeds of seepweed for food and doubtless the Death Valley Indians did the same.

VALLEY FLOOR, ALKALI FLATS; SHRUB

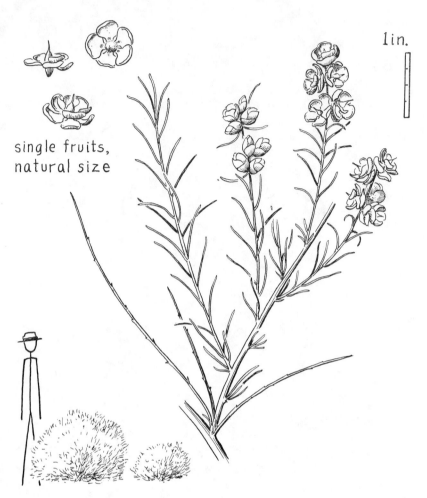

single fruits,
natural size

1 in.

WHITE BURROBRUSH *Hymenoclea salsola* Sunflower family

In almost any wash and along small drainage courses in the alluvial fans one can find the soft yellow-green mounds of the burrobrush. Summer showers as well as winter rains bring out a new growth of young stems and thread-like leaves. The flowers (the male and female ones are separated) are not conspicuous, but the fruits are interesting and attractive. The shining, white or pink-tinged, dry scales are fastened spirally to a hard central core. When young the fruits are shaped like small dry rosebuds; when old the scales spread horizontally from the central core. This and related species are widely distributed in the west. It has been called cheese-bush because of the odor of the crushed foliage, but it does not smell like the cheese most persons are fond of.

VALLEY FLOOR AND FANS, WASHES; SHRUB

BUR-SAGE   *Ambrosia dumosa*   Sunflower family

John C. Fremont, on his second expedition to the West on which he collected other plants of botanical interest, collected bur-sage on the desert at the Mojave River. In his report published in 1845 he consider-ed that it occurred as abundantly as creosotebrush. In Death Valley it is common well up on the slopes and follows down the broader washes to lower elevations.

The low, stiffly spreading bushes are usually well under 3 feet. They have whitish stems and rather small, grey-green, lobed leaves. The male and female flowers are separated on the flowering stalk and the spiny burs which contain the seeds do not blow away in the wind as quickly as do the small flowers which bear the pollen.

It has been called burrobush by some and burroweed by others. They say that burros and sheep prefer this bitter aromatic shrub.

VALLEY FLOOR AND FANS; SHRUB

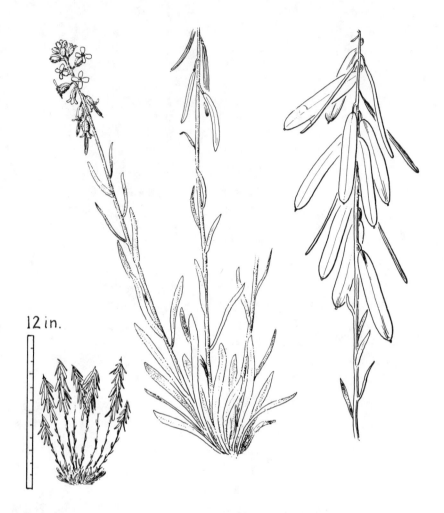

12 in.

BLUE-PODDED ROCKCRESS *Arabis glaucovalvula* Mustard family

This perennial rockcress is more conspicuous in fruit than in flower. The broad pendent pods are about an inch and one-half long and nearly a quarter of an inch broad, and are of a bluish purple cast in color. The flowers are pale pinkish purple and are sharply reflexed after flowering. The plants are a foot or less in height. They are limited to the Mojave Desert area, but other kinds of rockcress occur in this area. One which may be noticed is the beautiful rockcress *(Arabis pulchra)*. It has bright purple flowers and more slender pods which are much longer and fewer than the one pictured.

UPPER DESERT SLOPES AND PINYON-JUNIPER WOODLAND;
HERB; PURPLE

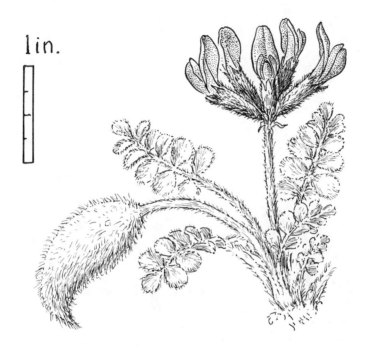

1 in.

Death Valley Locoweed   *Astragalus funereus*   Pea family

The growth habit of this species is much like the crimson locoweed. The pea-shaped flowers are shades of purple mixed with white, and the tubular calyx has an abundance of black hairs which contrast with the white hairs of the rest of the plant. The pods are large and woolly, and when ripe the stalks on which they grow bend over, half concealing the pods in the leaves. As you may guess from the name, this *Astragalus* was described from Death Valley and is found only in the Funeral Range and nearby mountains of Nevada. There are other locoweeds with woolly pods that have much the same coloring, but they differ from this rare species in length of floral parts and in size of pods.

Upper desert slopes; Herb; Purple

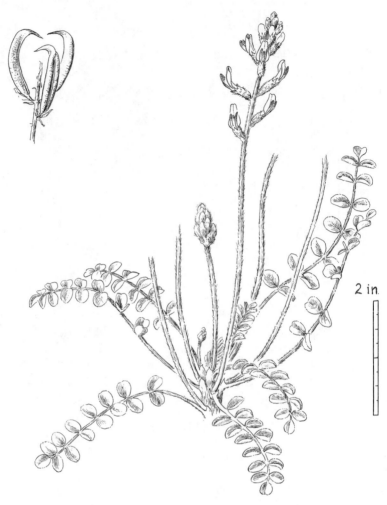

2 in.

LAYNE LOCOWEED   *Astragalus layneae*   Pea family

This plant has a creeping rhizome with one or more stems a half a foot or more tall rising erect from the ground. The leaflets are hairy but not so dense as to conceal the green beneath. The flowers spread away from the flower stalk and, though many, are well spaced. They are better than a half-inch long including the dark tubular calyx, and the separate parts of the flower are tipped with purple and are white below. The pods are hard, hairy, narrow and pointed. They are more or less erect and curve inward toward the stalk in a half circle. This species, and you might say a couple of "cousins" which (for one thing) differ conspicuously in the way the ripe pods grow on the stalks, are native in the Death Valley region, the Mojave Desert, and western Nevada.

UPPER DESERT SLOPES; HERB; PURPLE

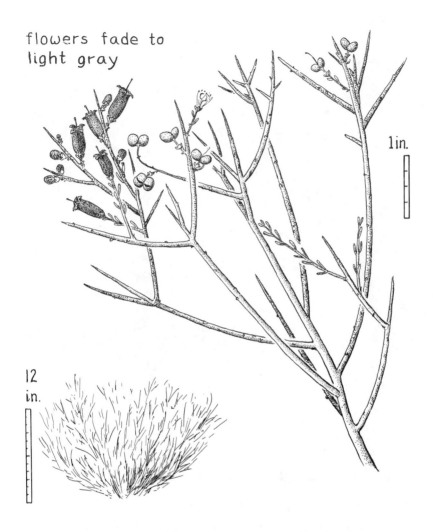

flowers fade to
light gray

1 in.

12
in.

Mojave Desert-Rue *Thamnosma montana* Rue family

The entire desert-rue plant is dull green and covered with small warty glands, even to the stalked two-lobed fruits which remain for a long time on the bushes. The petals of the flower and the narrow leaves, which soon drop off from the round green stems, are less warty. The petals are of so deep a purple color that they appear to be almost black. This species is to be found from southern Utah to California and south into northern Mexico. It has been reported that the Panamint Indians thought the crushed stems an aid in healing wounds.

Upper desert slopes and pinyon-juniper woodland;
Shrub; Purple

81

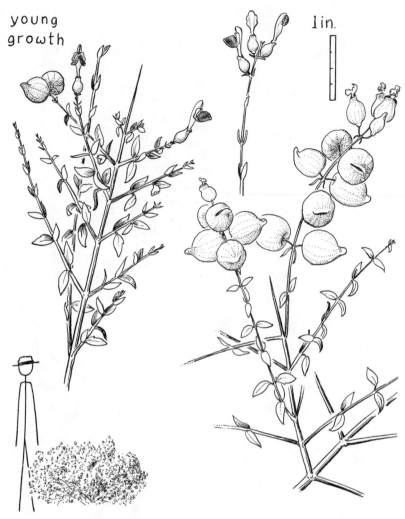

young growth

1 in.

MEXICAN BLADDERSAGE *Salazaria mexicana* Mint family

Perhaps the most interesting thing about this desert shrub is the enlarged papery calyx which encloses the fruit. The fruit actually consists of four little nutlets—four nutlets being a characteristic of the mint family. The shrubs are two to three feet high and the greenish white, somewhat spiny branches spreading at almost right angles make a dense tangle. The leaves are rather sparse. Bladder-sage is what is known in botanical circles as a monotypic genus. In other words there are no other species in the genus, unless some-one finds a new kind. It is common in northern Mexican deserts and grows as far north as Utah and Nevada.

UPPER DESERT SLOPES; SHRUB; PURPLE

82

SWEETLEAF WILDROSE   *Rosa woodsii gratissima*   Rose family

The wildrose certainly should be included in a list of Death Valley wildflowers. After all, one of the entrances to the valley goes through a canyon named for it. It is not restricted to Wildrose Canyon. Other canyons in the surrounding mountains, where streams flow at least part of the year, support wildroses which grow among the willow thickets and other shrubs that are companions of streams. Everyone recognizes a wildrose, but telling the difference between the kinds of wildroses poses a real problem. It is a variable genus.

UPPER SLOPES AND PINYON-JUNIPER WOODLAND; SHRUB; PINK

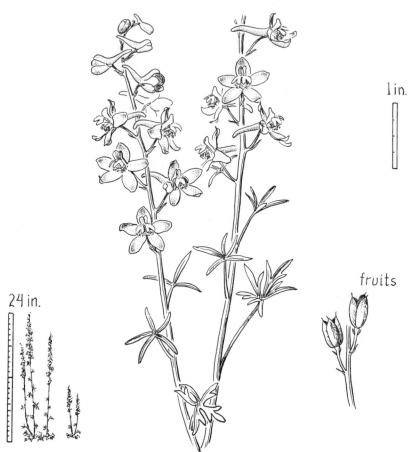

1 in.

fruits

24 in.

PARISH LARKSPUR   *Delphinium parishii*   Crowfoot family

There are several kinds of plants in Death Valley National Monument that have blue flowers, but only one other, the blue flax of the limber-bristlecone pine woodland, that is the sky blue of the Parish larkspur. The plants are not very tall—usually a foot and a half to two feet high—and grow in a spotty fashion among the gray-green shrubs of sagebrush in the pinyon belt or with other shrubs that grow on the higher desert slopes. It is found in like situations in other desert ranges. It even is found sometimes in the upper limits of the creosotebush scrub. This is another example where the species name honors a botanist and collector. Samuel B. Parish contributed much to our knowledge of California desert plants in the days when travel on desert roads was rough. One of his last major trips was to Death Valley in 1915 under the auspices of the Carnegie Institution.

UPPER DESERT SLOPES AND PINYON-JUNIPER WOODLAND;
HERB; BLUE

fruits

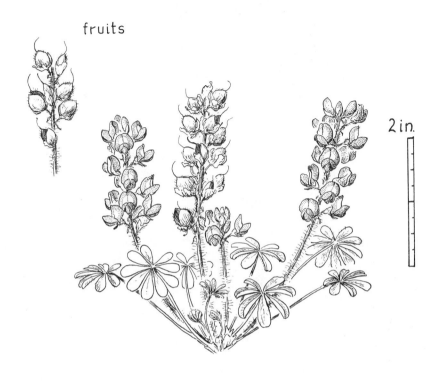

2 in.

YELLOWEYE LUPINE *Lupinus flavoculatus* Pea family

A splash of blue in loose soil at higher elevations in Inyo and San Bernardino counties and adjacent Nevada will probably turn out to be plants of this species. The sparsely hairy leaves are basal. The flowering stem, three to ten inches high, is densely set with violet-blue, pea-shaped flowers, each of which has a bright yellow spot on the upright banner. The pods are short and almost round.

UPPER DESERT SLOPES AND PINYON-JUNIPER WOODLAND;
HERB; BLUE

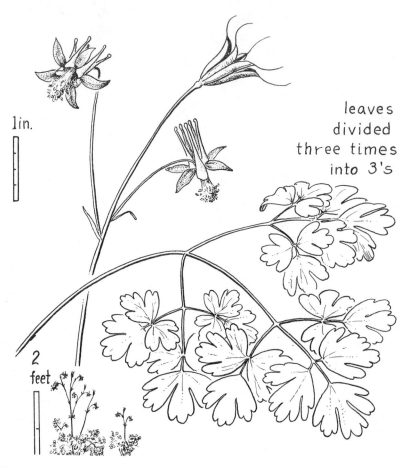

leaves
divided
three times
into 3's

1in.

2
feet

DESERT COLUMBINE   *Aquilegia shockleyi*   Crowfoot family

If you should be fortunate enough to see this red and yellow columbine by some spring or running stream in the canyons of mountains around Death Valley, you will probably think you have seen the same columbine before in other mountains in the west far removed from the desert area. The coloring of the drooping flowers is much the same as those, but the red or yellowish red spurs are more slender. A more obvious difference is in the faintly bluish basal leaves, which are triternate instead of biternate; in other words, they are divided three times into threes instead of two times into threes. The plants grow to a height of one and one-half to two and one-half feet. Desert columbine is not uncommon in desert ranges in Nevada and eastern California.

UPPER DESERT SLOPES AND PINYON-JUNIPER WOODLAND, STREAMBANKS; HERB; RED

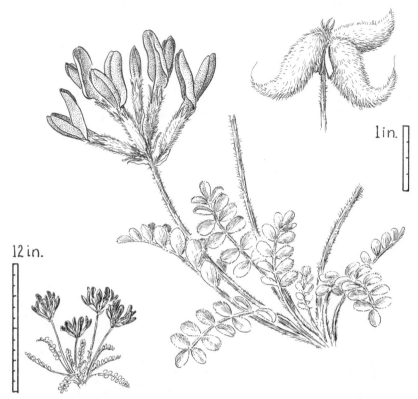

1 in.

12 in.

There are literally hundreds of species of *Astragalus* in the world. California alone has about a hundred different kinds, and to narrow the field still further, more than fifteen kinds are found in Death Valley and the surrounding desert ranges. Though there is a combination of characters that makes certain plants unmistakably species of the genus *Astragalus,* there are quite a lot of different shapes and sizes in the pods, even in the few kinds in Death Valley. They may be large and woolly, papery and shaped like bladders, narrow and stiffer than parchment, thin-walled and resembling tiny bean pods, and some even like irregular-shaped small nuts.

SCARLET LOCOWEED   *Astragalus coccineus*   Pea family

When in bloom this is one of the showiest plants that California deserts can offer, even if it is only a low-growing perennial herb. The leaves (divided into several leaflets) are silvery with dense tangled hairs and set off to advantage the large, bright red flowers on the many flower stalks. The stalks rise above the leaves three to five inches. The peashaped blossoms are an inch to an inch and one-half long. The pods are somewhat longer and densely clothed with wool.

UPPER DESERT SLOPES AND PINYON-JUNIPER WOODLAND; HERB; RED

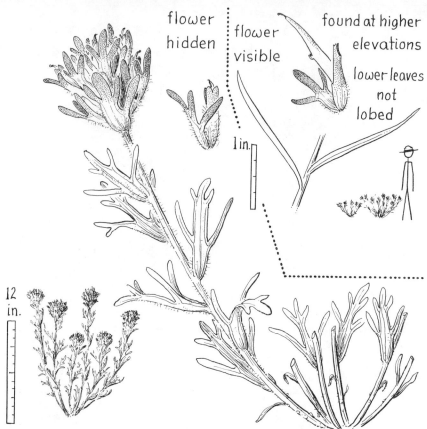

flower
hidden

flower
visible

found at higher
elevations

lower leaves
not
lobed

1 in.

12
in.

DESERT CASTILLEJA (DESERT INDIAN PAINTBRUSH)
Castilleja chromosa   Figwort family

This is a desert wildflower than can be accurately identified from a moving automobile. Even the driver with his eyes on the road will catch the flash of scarlet from the occasional plants of desert castilleja growing up among the low shrubs along the road. The actual flowers are scarcely visible, as they are hidden in the scarlet-tipped calyx, but the several stems end in a "brush" of scarlet-tipped leafy bracts. The plants are not only natives of southwestern deserts but also of the sagebrush plains as far north as Wyoming.

WYOMING PAINTEDCUP (LINARIA-LEAF CASTILLEJA)
Castilleja linariaefolia   Figwort family

One other castilleja is found in Death Valley but often at higher elevations than the desert castilleja. The plants are much taller (up to three feet) and not so brilliantly colored as the preceding, and the red and green flowers are longer than the bracts and calyx. (Illustrated on the upper right.)

UPPER DESERT SLOPES; HERB; RED

88

2 in.

DESERT MARIPOSA   *Calochortus kennedyi*   Lily family

The west is blessed with many species of this beautiful genus of the lily family. Various kinds of Calochortus, because of the shape of the petals or the hairs that sometimes cover them, have been called delightfully descriptive names: star tulip, pussy ears, fairy lantern, globe tulip. By far the most striking of them all is the group with large open flowers which are known as mariposas (butterflies in Spanish). The desert mariposa, which occurs in Death Valley as well as other parts of California, Arizona and Nevada, grows in heavy soil. The stems, topped with one to six flowers, are three to ten or more inches high and rise from deep-seated bulbs. The satiny petals (one to two inches long) are marked with purplish black at the base and may be vermillion, orange, or yellow—more often yellow in the Death Valley area.

UPPER DESERT SLOPES; HERB; YELLOW

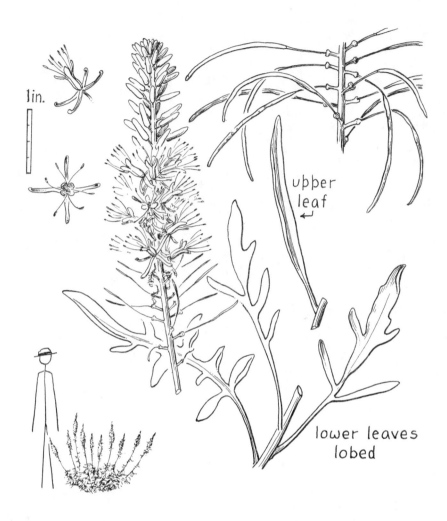

1 in.

upper
leaf
←

lower leaves
lobed

DESERT PRINCESPLUME   *Stanleya pinnata*   Mustard family

The desert princesplume grows in this area and is often found at low elevations. The plants are about as high as the Panamint princesplume but are more often branched; the leaves are lobed and not entire, but the flowers are much the same as those of the other species. In years when all the flowers set seed the long slender curving pods on the tall flowering stalks (in both species) are as striking as the flowers. The desert princesplume is much more widespread than the Panamint princesplume and is found as far east as the plains of the Dakotas.

UPPER DESERT SLOPES AND VALLEY FLOOR; HERB; YELLOW

90

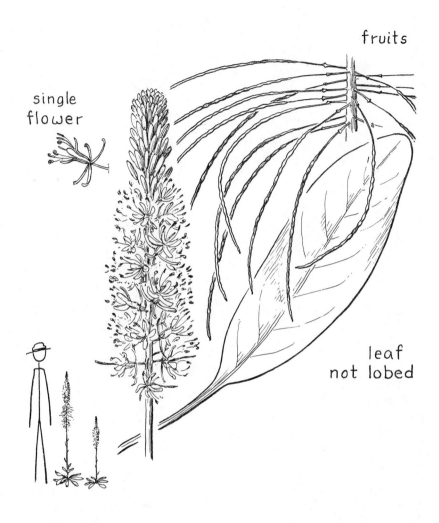

fruits

single
flower

leaf
not lobed

PANAMINT PRINCESPLUME   *Stanleya elata*   Mustard family

This member of the mustard family grows on the slopes and mesas from about 3,000 to 3,500 feet. The tall unbranched plants (two to five feet high) are easily spotted by the long plume of yellow flowers which rise well above the rather large, entire leaves. This grows only in southern Nevada, northwestern Arizona, and the Death Valley region.

UPPER DESERT SLOPES; HERB; YELLOW

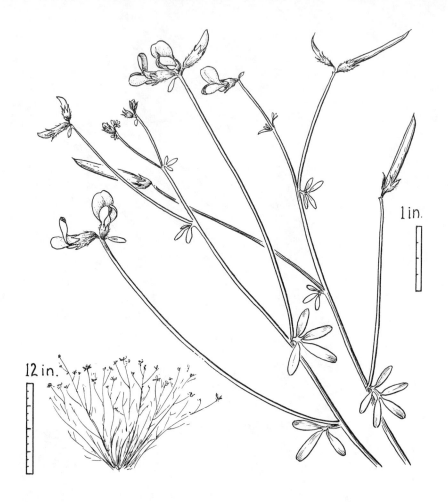

1 in.

12 in.

SHRUBBY DEERVETCH   *Lotus rigidus*   Pea family

The shrubby deervetch is a half-shrubby perennial with several green stems rising from the woody base. The leaves, divided into three to five leaflets, are very apt to fall, leaving the stems and branches completely bare. The slender stalks that bear the clusters of two or three pea-shaped flowers are about an inch and one-half long, often longer. The yellow flowers are showy in spite of their small size (about one-half an inch) and the back of the upper petal (banner) is often tinged with red. The species is widespread throughout the western deserts but seldom abundant in one place. In some books it is listed under the generic name of *Lotus,* while in others it is found under the name *Hosackia.* The name used is a matter of botanical interpretation as to whether the plants belong to a world-wide genus or to one that is limited to the west.

UPPER DESERT SLOPES; HERB; YELLOW

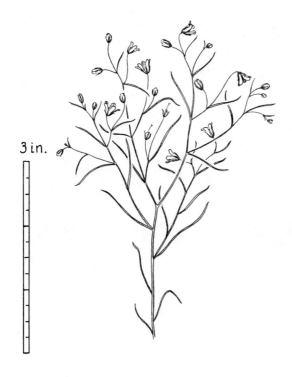

3 in.

THREADSTEM GILIA   *Gilia filiformis*   Phlox family

The threadstem gilia has clear yellow flowers shaped like little bells; these are scattered among the thread-like leaves on the small plants. They will be found on gravelly mesas sometimes to elevations as high as 5,500 feet, though often much lower.

UPPER DESERT SLOPES; HERB; YELLOW

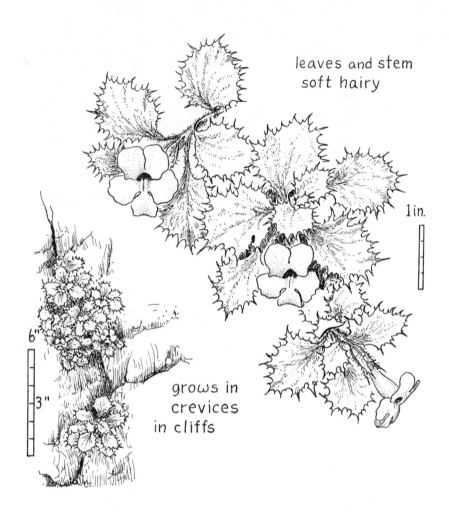

leaves and stem
soft hairy

1 in.

6"

3"

grows in
crevices
in cliffs

ROCKLADY MAURANDYA   *Maurandya petrophila*   Figwort family

Rocklady is perhaps the rarest wildflower in the monument. So far this attractive little rock plant has been found in only a very few localities—hanging from the crevices of limestone cliffs. The flowers are pale yellow with a deeper yellow throat. The leaves are an inch or more long and wide and edged with bristly teeth.

UPPER DESERT SLOPES, CANYON WALLS; HERB; YELLOW

94

2 inches

2 feet

leaves
thick
and silvery

COVILLE ENCELIOPSIS (PANAMINT DAISY) *Enceliopsis argophylla grandiflora* Sunflower family

Enceliopsis is known locally as the Panamint daisy. "Daisy" is far too modest a name for this magnificent flower, which is four to five inches across. The flowers rise a foot or more above the basal tufts of large silvery leaves. The plants grow on dry rocky ledges, probably in soil in which there is gypsum, because its closest relative *(Enceliopsis argophylla)* is known to grow only in gypsum deposits in southern Nevada and Utah. By all means stop and take a picture, but do not pick them. There are too few of them about for others to enjoy.

UPPER DESERT SLOPES; HERB; YELLOW

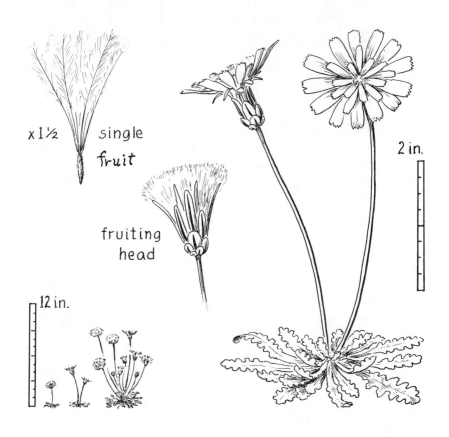

x 1½ single fruit

fruiting head

2 in.

12 in.

ANISOCOMA *Anisocoma acaulis* Sunflower family

This small desert annual (three to eight inches high) grows in both California deserts and in the desert areas of Nevada and Arizona. It grows in sand or gravelly soil mostly at lower elevations, but it also can be found at elevations up to 6,000 feet if conditions are right for its growth. Few to several naked stalks rise from the close rosette of divided leaves with a single, pale yellow flower head on each stalk. Anisocoma is at its best in fruit. The bracts under the heads are papery and strawcolored. Each one (both the short rounded lower ones and the narrow upper ones) is marked with a conspicuous maroon line and sometimes, in addition, maroon dots. The feathered fluff on the fruits is longer than the bracts, so that the whole flower head may be an inch or an inch and a half long.

UPPER DESERT SLOPES; HERB; YELLOW

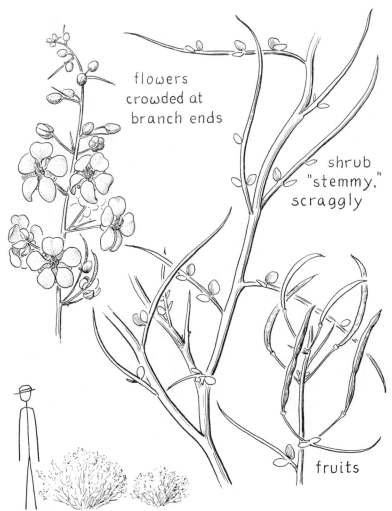

flowers crowded at branch ends

shrub "stemmy," scraggly

fruits

DESERT SENNA *Cassia armata* Pea family

Most of the year, desert senna is just another desert shrub that is hard to identify because it has no leaves, flowers or fruits; only smooth, grayish green stems almost a quarter of an inch in diameter that taper to a point. In the flowering season the shrub presents quite a different picture, as the tops of the now green stems are covered with yellow blossoms about an inch broad, and the leaves, though rather sparse, are interesting to examine. As in most members of the pea family a leaf is made up of small leaflets fastened to a central stemlike vein (midrib). In desert senna the midrib is flat and nearly as broad as each of the leaflets are wide. It is a native of the California, Nevada and Arizona deserts and even extends into north-western Mexico.

UPPER DESERT SLOPES; SHRUB; YELLOW

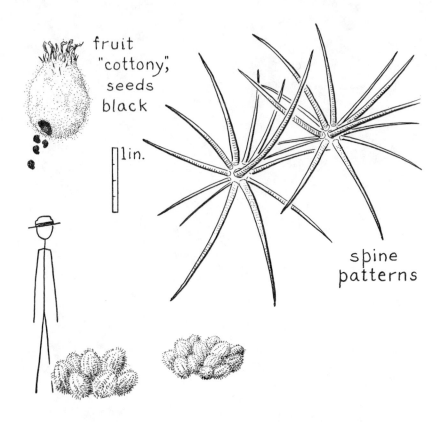

fruit "cottony", seeds black

1 in.

spine patterns

All the members of the cactus family that grow in the west have one thing in common—they have no leaves. The stems assume a fantastic variety of shapes. They may be flattened oval pads, branched canes, thick poles, huge "war clubs," large or small cylinders, heads or "barrels." They are always green and fleshy though the surface may be pretty well concealed by different kinds of spines. Several different kinds are found in Death Valley National Monument.

COTTONTOP ECHINOCACTUS *Echinocactus polycephalus*
Cactus family

As you drive down the alluvial fans, through the desert shrubs you see clusters a foot or so high of ribbed spiny heads—sometimes as many as forty in a clump. They are beset with groups of strong flattish spines of unequal length. The yellow flowers, which grow only at the tops of the heads, are half-buried in white wool, and the dry fruit appears to be a woolly ball.

UPPER DESERT SLOPES; SHRUB; YELLOW

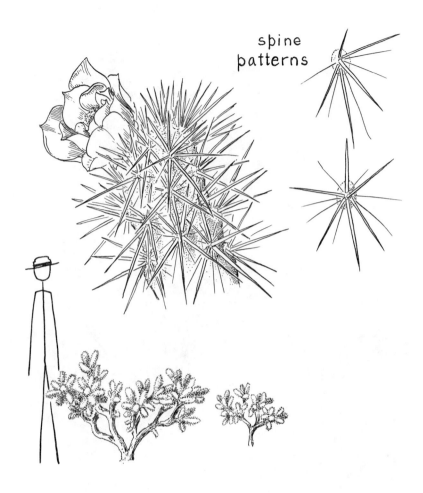

spine
patterns

There are two types of growth in the widespread genus *Opuntia:* those in which the joints are flattened and those in which the joints are rounded and the plants angularly branched. The former are usually called pricklypears, the latter cholla.

STRAWTOP CHOLLA   *Opuntia echinocarpa*   Cactus family

This cholla usually has a distinct trunk and many short (four to six inches) branching joints. The whole plant is copiously covered with pale rigid spines. The flowers are greenish yellow, with sometimes a tinge of red on the outer petals, and blend rather than contrast with the appearance of the plant. The fruits are dry and spiny and harvesting them would be a real problem to the small hungry creatures of the desert.

UPPER DESERT SLOPES; SHRUB; YELLOW

99

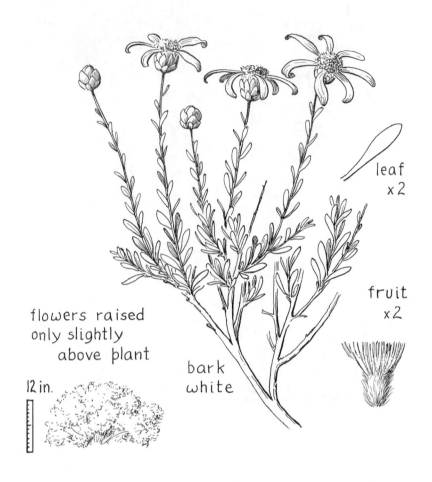

leaf
x2

fruit
x2

flowers raised
only slightly
above plant

12 in.

bark
white

SHOCKLEY GOLDENHEAD   *Acamptopappus shockleyi*
Sunflower family

Shockley goldenhead would be an ideal plant in a cactus garden if it could be made to grow in cultivation. It is a spreading shrub with woody stems rising to a height of one-half foot to about two feet. The tongue-shaped leaves are small and grayish green. The yellow flower heads are often two inches broad and are borne on slender stalks above the leaves, making quite a show in spring. Like so many desert shrubs it will respond to late summer rain, and one may have the pleasure of seeing it in flower again in early fall. It grows in southwestern Nevada and eastern California.

UPPER DESERT SLOPES; SHRUB; YELLOW

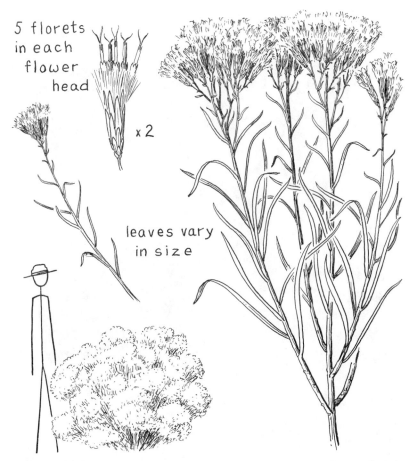

5 florets in each flower head

x 2

leaves vary in size

RUBBER RABBITBRUSH   *Chrysothamnus nauseosus*   Sunflower family

More than one subspecies or variety of rubber rabbitbrush is to be found in the monument, as well as five or six other species which look very different in size, leaves and growth habit from the gray-leaved, fall-flowering one you see pictured. The shrubs of the rubber rabbitbrush are three or four feet high, are bushy, and the branches are quite flexible and leafy, though the plants have a tendency to drop their leaves early. The scientific name *"nauseosus"* is a misnomer for the plant has a pleasing aromatic odor. Some forms of it have been found to produce some rubber, but for various practical reasons it has not been worthwhile to obtain rubber from it commercially. It grows on flats and along broad watercourses in loose soil, often with sagebrush, and it, or its several subspecies, occurs commonly in the west.

UPPER DESERT SLOPES AND PINYON-JUNIPER WOODLAND;
SHRUB; YELLOW

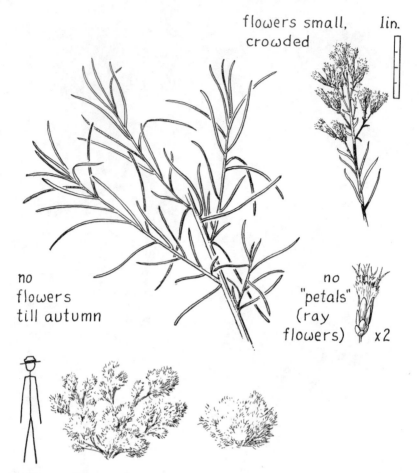

flowers small, crowded

lin.

no flowers till autumn

no "petals" (ray flowers) x2

DESERT RABBITBRUSH   *Chrysothamnus paniculatus*
Sunflower family

Desert rabbitbrush is a branching shrub usually five to six feet high with aromatic needlelike green leaves and rather stout, straight, tan-colored, trunklike stems. It grows in the sand and gravel of the canyon washes or even on the fans in the stream courses. It is nearly always infected with a fungus disease that makes black bands around the young growth. It is not to be confused with the sprucebush *(Peucephyllum schottii),* a darker stemmed open shrub with a tree-like growth, which flowers early and grows in the same places. The desert rabbitbrush and all the many other kinds of rabbitbrush, both tall and short, that grow around the Death Valley area bloom in the early fall and their masses of yellow flowers furnish color at that time of the year.

UPPER DESERT SLOPES, WASHES; SHRUB; YELLOW

102

WHITE BRITTLEBUSH (INCIENSO) *Encelia farinosa*
Sunflower family

White brittlebush is one of the more striking shrubs of the monument. The symmetrical plants, densely clothed with leaves, grow on the basal slopes of the ranges, in the small draws and canyons, and less commonly in the washes. Even in leaf it is conspicuous among the dark rocks; doubly so when covered with a mass of small sunflowers about an inch broad borne on flower stalks that much surpass the leaves. Both the common names that have been applied to this desert shrub are appropriate. The leaves are silvery white and the stems extremely brittle. Although Acton encelia *(Encelia virginensis actonii),* on the right, much resembles the preceding, each flower stalk in this species bears only a single flower head instead of bearing several to a stalk, which is characteristic of the brittlebush. It grows more commonly in washes and is not distributed as widely as its relative, the brittlebush.

UPPER DESERT SLOPES AND VALLEY FLOOR AND FANS;
SHRUB; YELLOW

BROOM SNAKEWEED   *Gutierrezia sarothrae*   Sunflower family

THREADLEAF SNAKEWEED   *Gutierrezia microcephala*
Sunflower family

When you are traveling in the southwest in the late summer
months, some species of snakeweed will make their presence known
to you by the areas covered with golden yellow. Though the flower
heads are tiny, literally hundreds may cover the bushy perennial
herbs or small shrubs. Two kinds grow in Death Valley National
Monument. The threadleaf snakeweed (left) forms a small slender-
stemmed, rounded bush on which the flower heads are clustered
in tight little bunches at the ends of the branchlets. Sometimes only
one ray floret occurs on each head. The flower heads of broom snakeweed (right) usually have four or five rays each, and are not so
tightly clustered. One form of broom snakeweed is only five or six
inches high and may have only a single flower head at the ends of
the branches.

UPPER DESERT SLOPES TO LIMBER-BRISTLECONE PINE WOODLAND;
SHRUBS; YELLOW

1 in.

leaf edges
roll under

DEATH VALLEY GOLDENEYE   *Viguiera reticulata*
Sunflower family

Death Valley goldeneye, as its name implies, is restricted to the Death Valley region though it is found in adjacent ranges outside of the monument borders. The flowers of this shrub are yellow, are several to many, and are borne in long-stemmed clusters well above the mound of leafy stems. It is not to be confused with brittlebush *(Encelia farinosa)* which it much resembles in habit. One look at the leaves will end the confusion, for though the leaves are white they are quite broad and the leaf blades do not taper into the stems as do those of brittlebush. In addition, the veinlets as well as the veins of the leaves are prominent and give a net-like appearance especially on the underside of the leaf, which is harsh to the touch in age. Though the shrub is evergreen, the skeleton leaves of earlier growth stay on the plant dead white among the greenish white of the living leaves. Nevada showy goldeneye *(Viguiera multiflora nevadensis)* is more common in the southern Great Basin than here. This narrow-leaved herb (shown at right) grows on the pinyon-juniper slopes.

UPPER DESERT SLOPES AND PINYON-JUNIPER WOODLAND;
SHRUB; YELLOW

2 in.

Weakstem Mariposa   *Calochortus flexuosus*   Lily family

For a mariposa this one has an unusual habit of growth. The stems are not erect but they more or less twine on the branches of shrubs or merely lean over on the rocky ground. The plants can reach a length of eighteen inches. The flowers are few, not more than four as a rule. The petals, which are one to two inches long, are white tinged with lilac and are beautifully marked basally with a yellow band and a purple spot. This is typically a plant of the Great Basin area and is found from the eastern part of the California deserts to southwestern Colorado. It grows in the upper reaches of the creosotebush belt into the higher areas where big sagebrush grows.

Upper desert slopes; Herb; White

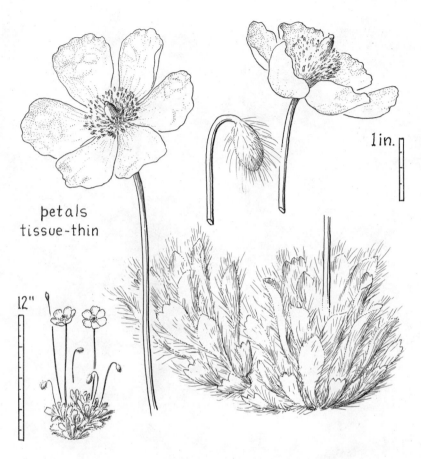

petals
tissue-thin

1in.

12"

DESERT BEARPOPPY *Arctomecon merriamii* Poppy family

The bearpoppy is a member of the poppy family that grows only in the Death Valley region and southern Nevada. If one excludes the Panamint daisy, it is perhaps the most strikingly beautiful plant in the monument. The large white flowers appear singly on the tall naked stems. The bluish green leaves are fan-shaped and often toothed at the top, and the buds are densely covered with long straight silver hairs. It is called "bearpoppy" because of this covering of hair. It is rarely seen, as it grows only occasionally in the higher washes and canyons. Another kind of bearpoppy with several yellow flowers on a single stem grows in southern Nevada. Though this one has the scientific name *Arctomecon californica,* it has not yet been collected within the state boundary.

UPPER DESERT SLOPES; HERB; WHITE

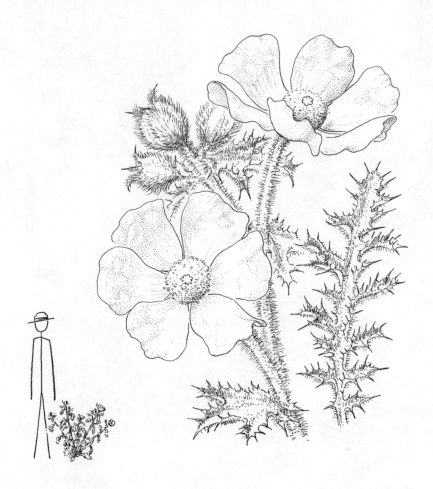

DESERT PRICKLEPOPPY *Argemone munita argentea* Poppy family

Pricklepoppies of some kind or other grow all over the arid southwest and Mexico. Superficially they look much alike in growth form and flowers but differ by such characters as the kinds of hairs and spines on the foliage, the arrangement of spines on the hard fruits, and so forth. The plant is beautiful to look at, but you will regret touching it because of the spines. The large flowers are about four inches broad and the white petals are textured like tissue paper. The flowers of other species and subspecies of the southwestern states look much like ours. The lobed large spiny leaves are bluish white. The plants are two or three feet tall and unbranched. It is mostly found on flats and washes around the 3,000 or 4,500 foot level.

UPPER DESERT SLOPES, WASHES; HERB; WHITE

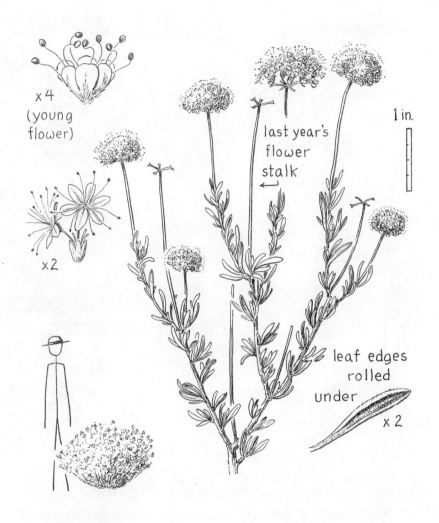

x4
(young
flower)

x2

last year's
flower
stalk

1 in.

leaf edges
rolled
under

x2

ROSEMARY ERIOGONUM   *Eriogonum fasciculatum polifolium*
Buckwheat family

There are many varieties of this species of eriogonum, some of them occurring on the ocean side of the mountains. This evergreen shrub has small, narrow, grayish green leaves set closely in bunches along the stems with the leafless flower stalks surpassing the leafy stems. The whitish flowers are tiny but conspicuous by their very abundance in the flower heads.

UPPER DESERT SLOPES; SHRUB; WHITE

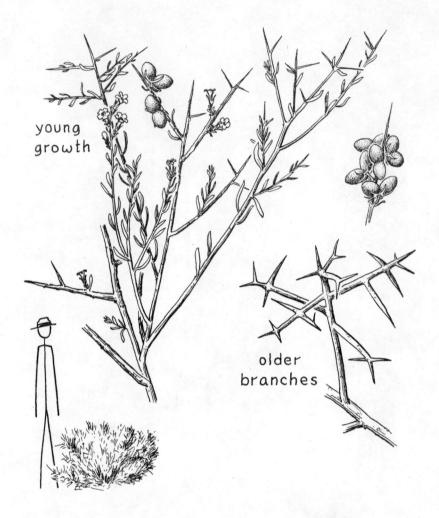

young
growth

older
branches

SPINY MENODORA   *Menodora spinescens*   Olive family

Spiny menodora grows on desert slopes of the Mojave Desert northward and eastward to Nevada and Arizona at elevations of 3,500 to about 6,500 feet. Many of the desert plants have spines, stinging hairs or branches ending in spines. Of the last category, spiny menodora is one of the more formidable. The stout green branches of the bushes spread at angles, and each of the many branches ends in a sharp point. Only the young, not yet thickened branches are covered with the small leaves. The small tubular flowers are white with a tinge of pink, and the two-lobed fruits are covered with a translucent coat.

UPPER DESERT SLOPES; SHRUB; WHITE

110

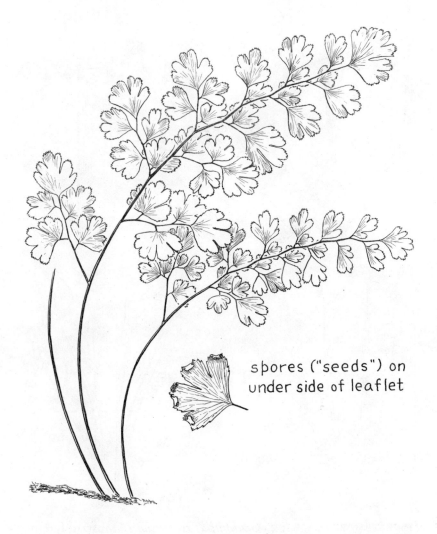

spores ("seeds") on
under side of leaflet

SOUTHERN MAIDENHAIR   *Adiantum capillus-veneris*   Fern family

Southern maidenhair is a delicate fern with many irregularly fan-shaped leaflets (pinnules) on the upper part of the slender, purplish black stalks and appears much like the one the florists use to set off their choice bouquets. This is not a plant that one thinks of meeting in so dry a place as Death Valley. It must have lots of moisture, however, and can be found growing in dripping seeps and springs or on the canyon walls in the ranges about the valley. Southern maidenhair is not restricted to this area and can be found in subtropical regions in both the Old and the New World.

UPPER DESERT SLOPES; SPRINGS, FERN

111

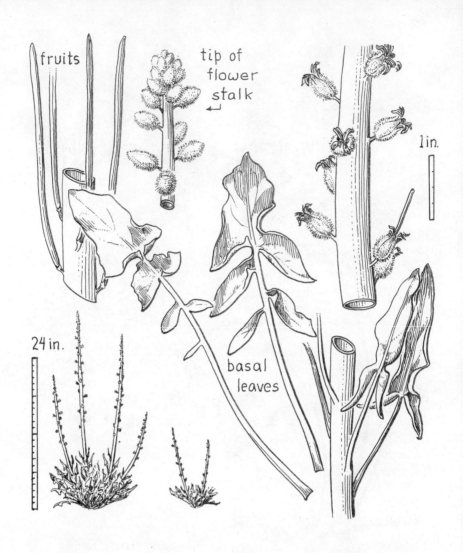

fruits

tip of
flower
stalk

1 in.

24 in.

basal
leaves

THICKSTEM WILDCABBAGE *Caulanthus crassicaulis* Mustard family

Coville reported in notes published on plant materials used by the Panamint Indians, that leaves of this and other plants of the mustard family were first boiled and then redried before the Indians considered them ready for eating. Thickstem wildcabbage grows one to three feet high and the leaves are bluish green. The flowers, which have hairy purplish sepals and purple petals, are set along the thickened flower stalk and the pods are erect. This is a species of the Great Basin rather than one of the southern deserts. Don't confuse it with squaw-cabbage *(Caulanthus inflatus)*, which has a very thick flower stalk and grows on the Mojave Desert.

PINYON-JUNIPER WOODLAND; HERB; PURPLE

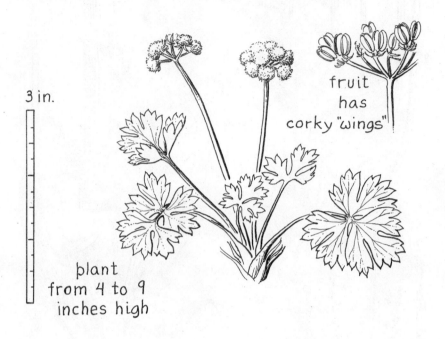

3 in.

fruit
has
corky "wings"

plant
from 4 to 9
inches high

GILMAN CYMOPTERUS *Cymopterus gilmanii* Carrot family

Most of the members of the carrot family that one meets have leaves much more finely divided than those of this species. The leaves, which are always basal, are orbicular in outline, and the few divisions are broadly triangular and toothed. The little bractlets around the purplish flowers are longer than the flowers themselves, and the wings on the fruit are wider than the fruit itself. Gilman cymopterus grows in canyons in the mountains about Death Valley and in southern Nevada. Often plants are given scientific names to honor the one who first collected them. This was collected by French Gilman, who did so much in the 1930's in finding plants in Death Valley not heretofore known to occur there.

PINYON-JUNIPER WOODLAND, CANYONS; HERB; PURPLISH

113

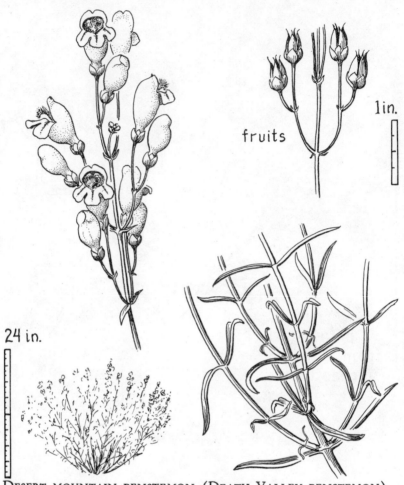

fruits

1 in.

24 in.

DESERT MOUNTAIN PENSTEMON (DEATH VALLEY PENSTEMON)
Penstemon fruticiformis   Figwort family

This is another plant that Coville found and later described in his report on the Death Valley Expedition. It grows in the desert mountains adjacent to Death Valley and a subspecies of it grows as far south as the San Bernardino Mountains. It forms a rounded shrub much branched from the base, but the stems do not make a dense mass. The leaves are narrow and bluish green. The flowers are an inch long and distinctly fat in the middle—a gibbous throat is the technical way of describing it. The flower has been variously described as rose-colored, as white with blue lobes, or as lavender with purplish lobes. The color probably changes with the age of the flower.

PINYON-JUNIPER WOODLAND AND UPPER DESERT SLOPES;
SHRUB; PURPLE

114

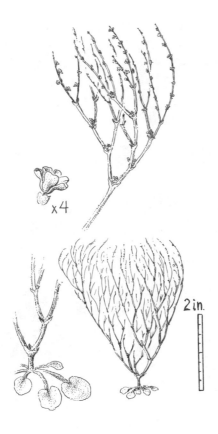

BIRDNEST ERIOGONUM (WHISKBROOM) *Eriogonum nidularium*
Buckwheat family

Birdnest eriogonum is found in other places in the Mojave Desert, but in the monument it is found in late summer in canyons and on upper desert slopes and with the junipers and pinyons. The small reddish (sometimes yellowish) flowers are set at regular intervals along the somewhat cobwebby stems, which branch and rebranch as this small annual (three to six inches high) lives out its short life span. The dried-up plants persist until the wind blows them away. They are readily recognizable by the dense mass of incurved branches which rather resembles old birds' nests. The scientific name given to this eriogonum is based on this resemblance.

PINYON-JUNIPER WOODLAND AND UPPER DESERT SLOPES; HERB; RED

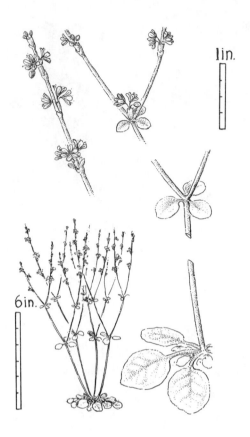

PANAMINT ERIOGONUM   *Eriogonum panamintense*
Buckwheat family

Along with the shrubs of rabbitbrush, sagebrush, and other woody
growth among the pinyons and junipers, there are many perennial herbs,
some of which are eriogonums. The Panamint eriogonum is found in
the mountains of the monument and in the other high desert ranges of
Inyo County east of the Sierra Nevada to those of western Nevada. The
plants have stalked felty white leaves at the base and at each joint of
the stem, and as it divides and redivides there is a collar of round white
leaves which reduce in size on the upper joints. The flowers are in small
clusters fitted tightly to the nearly upright stems.

PINYON-JUNIPER WOODLAND; HERB; PINKISH WHITE

116

PHLOX *Phlox longifolia* Phlox family

If you had this phlox in your rock garden, blooming as it does in the stony ground in the pinyon and limber pine forest, you would have something to boast about. However, it probably would not respond favorably to good garden care. The plants are four to eight inches high with several rather woody stems from a stout root. The leaves are narrow, gray-green and hairy. The pink flowers with their long tubes and flaring lobes often cover this small shrublet with a profusion of bloom. Until recently this plant was treated under the name *Phlox stansburyi*.

PINYON-JUNIPER AND LIMBER-BRISTLECONE PINE WOODLAND; HERB; PINK

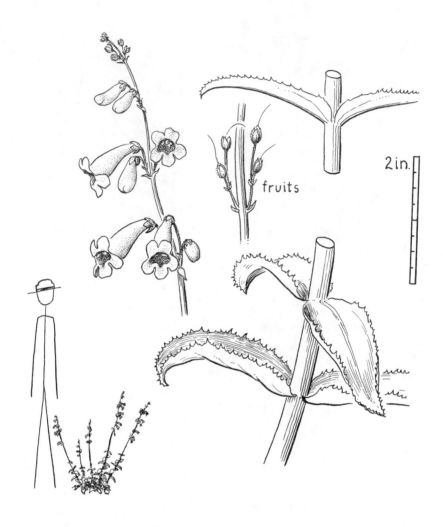

fruits

2 in.

PANAMINT PENSTEMON   *Penstemon floridus austinii*
Figwort family

This subspecies has a much less swollen look to the rose-pink corolla than that of the species which is found more commonly in the desert mountains north of Death Valley. Though the plants do not occur in great abundance in any one place, the individual plants one finds have several straight unbranched stems rising from the root to a height of two or three feet. The leaves below the flowers are bluish green and are margined with many small teeth. The flower stalk itself has some glandular hairs.

PINYON-JUNIPER WOODLAND AND UPPER DESERT SLOPES;
HERB; PINK

118

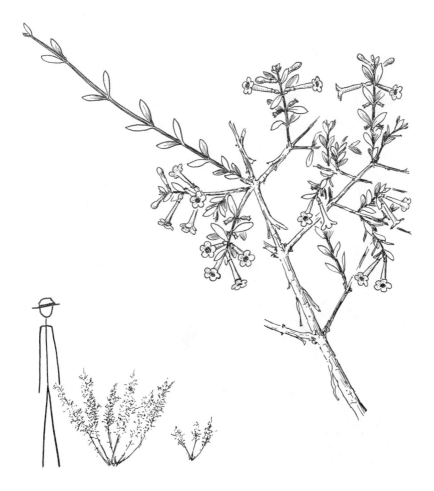

LONGFLOWER SNOWBERRY   (DESERT SNOWBERRY)
Symphoricarpos longiflorus   Honeysuckle family

This is an open shrub one to four feet high with rather slender erect stems. The bark of the old stems is gray and shreddy, while that of the younger stems and widely spreading branches and branchlets is smooth and brown. The small, pale blue-green leaves are clustered on the branchlets and it is in these clusters that the long-tubed, very fragrant flowers appear. The flower is more deeply colored on the outside than within. In fact the outside is about all one sees, as the flat-spreading lobes are only about one-fifth the length of the tube. The fruits are white and about one-half inch long. This snowberry seems to prefer limestone as a place to grow. It is rather common in the desert mountains of the Great Basin.

PINYON-JUNIPER WOODLAND, CANYONS; SHRUB; PINK

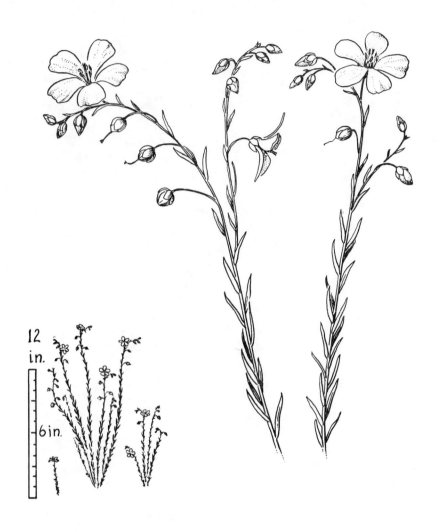

LEWIS FLAX   *Linum lewisii*   Flax family

The perennial blue flowered flax may be seen in late spring or early summer almost anywhere from the pinyon and juniper groves to the top of Telescope Peak. It will have a familiar look to you, and quite understandably, for this form or one very similar is a home garden favorite. The flowers are about an inch across. The leaves are small and bluish green. This widespread plant can be found in mountainous areas from Alaska and the Rocky Mountain region to Mexico. It is named in honor of its first collector, Meriwether Lewis of the Lewis and Clark Expedition.

PINYON-JUNIPER AND LIMBER-BRISTLECONE PINE WOODLAND; HERB; BLUE

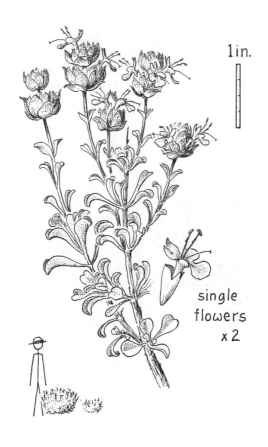

1in.

single
flowers
x 2

DESERT SAGE (PURPLE SAGE)   *Salvia dorrii*   Mint family

The desert sage of the higher mesas and canyons of the Death Valley region at elevations of 4,000 to 6,000 feet is a form which differs in some minor technical details from the one Zane Grey probably meant in his "Riders of the Purple Sage." The flowering stems with their purplish bracts and blue flowers surpass the compact whitish leafy bushes and all parts of it give off a very pleasing fragrance.

PINYON-JUNIPER WOODLAND; SHRUB; BLUE

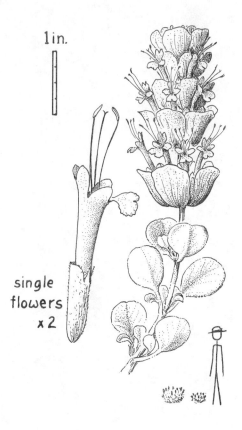

1 in.

single
flowers
x 2

THICKLEAF SAGE (ROSE SAGE)   *Salvia pachyphylla*   Mint family

Thickleaf sage much resembles the desert sage in the way it grows and in the shape of the leaves and in the pleasant odor. Though the flowers and bracts are in whorls around the flowering stem, the whorls are very close together and make an oblong head a few inches long. The flower bracts are much larger than those of desert sage and are rose-colored. They remain on the stems until the wind carries them off, long after the inch-long, deep blue flowers have fallen. The low shrubs are found in open places among the mountain-mahoganies and pinyons and also higher in the limber pine woodland, not only in the Death Valley region but south in desert mountain ranges to northern Baja California.

PINYON-JUNIPER AND LIMBER-BRISTLECONE PINE WOODLAND; SHRUB; BLUE

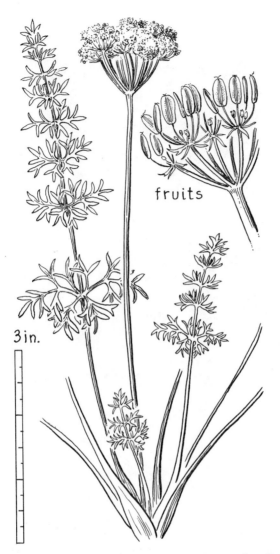

fruits

3 in.

PARRY LOMATIUM *Lomatium parryi* Carrot family

There are many species of *Lomatium* in the west but Parry lomatium occurs only in the desert ranges from the Death Valley region to southeastern Utah. It grows in rocky draws and around boulders in the pinyons and junipers. The leaves, though much divided, are long and rather narrow in outline and are all basal. The flowering stems are about as tall as the basal leaves and bear the small yellow flowers clustered at the ends of stalks which radiate from the main stem like the ribs of an umbrella.

PINYON-JUNIPER WOODLAND, CANYONS; HERB; YELLOW

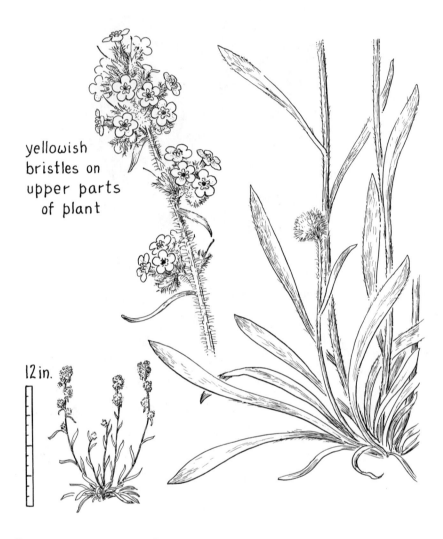

yellowish
bristles on
upper parts
of plant

12 in.

GOLDEN CRYPTANTHA (GOLDEN FORGET-ME-NOT)
Cryptantha confertiflora　Borage family

　　Golden cryptantha has several stems a foot or more high rising
from a woody base. Most of the leaves, which are silvery, are
crowded at the bases of the plants, and the golden yellow flowers,
which are nearly an inch across, are clustered toward the tops of the
stems. These attractive plants may occasionally be seen as one drives
through the pinyons. Like so many other plants of the Death Valley
region, golden cryptantha can be found in southern Nevada and
Utah as well as eastern California.

PINYON-JUNIPER WOODLAND; HERB; YELLOW

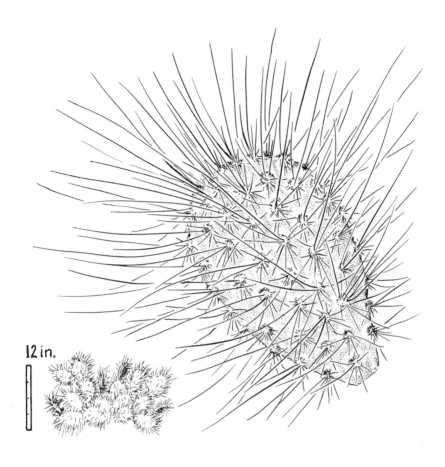

12 in.

GRIZZLY BEAR PRICKLYPEAR (OLD MAN PRICKLYPEAR)
Opuntia erinacea, O. erinacea ursina   Cactus family

These are low-growing plants with flattened pad-like joints which form mats that may rise to a height of a foot or so. They almost conceal themselves in their slender spines, particularly the variety *ursina*. On this the spines are three to six inches long, or even eight inches, and very flexible. The scientific and common names both imply a resemblance to the coarse fur of a bear. The flowers are yellow, though sometimes flushed with pink or red.

PINYON-JUNIPER WOODLAND; SHRUB; YELLOW

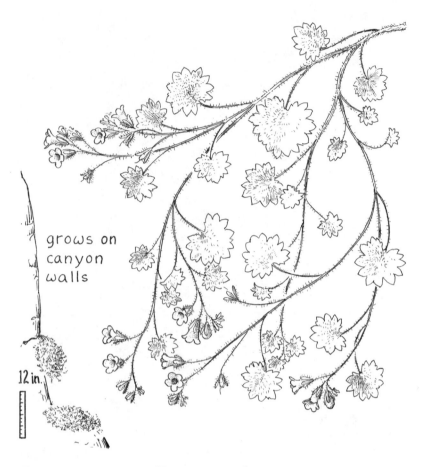

grows on
canyon
walls

12 in.

PANAMINT PHACELIA (PEARL-O-ROCK)
Phacelia perityloides   Waterleaf family

This phacelia looks very different from those more commonly seen about the monument. It grows only in crevices or cracks on canyon walls mostly of limestone at elevations of about 3,000 to 4,500 feet. The plants form densely leafy mounds or may, where water drips down the vertical cliffs, be seen in pendent masses hanging for a foot or more. The plant is a very showy thing if one is fortunate enough to see it in bloom. The small, rather short-stalked, white (with a purplish base) flowers are set off against the background of the small round sticky leaves. This is another plant that was first collected on the Death Valley Expedition in 1891, but it is also found in similar places in the limestone canyons of desert ranges in this general area.

PINYON-JUNIPER WOODLAND, CANYONS; HERB; WHITE

126

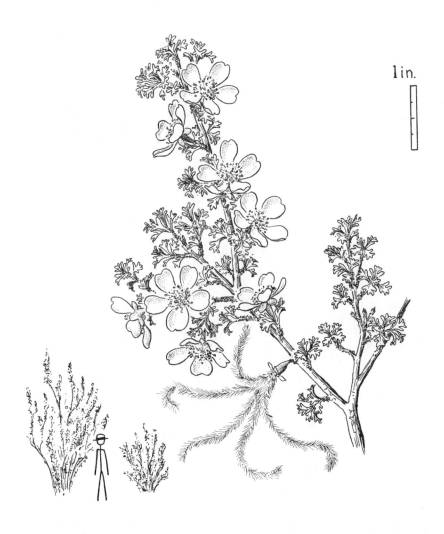

1 in.

STANSBURY CLIFFROSE *Cowania mexicana stansburiana* Rose family

Gnarled and wide-branching and shaggy-barked though this eight to ten foot evergreen shrub is, it nevertheless is a wonderful sight to see when covered with cream-colored rose-like flowers. It is almost as attractive in fruit, when each seed in a single flower develops a plumy tail one or two inches long. These plumes resemble those of its relative, the mountain-mahogany, with which it grows, but that small tree has but one plumed tail per flower and no petals at all. The small hard leaves are three- to five-parted.

PINYON-JUNIPER WOODLAND; SHRUB; WHITE

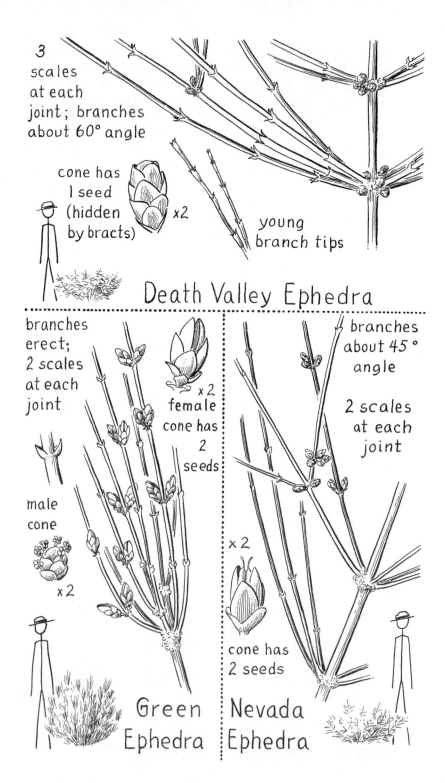

3 scales at each joint; branches about 60° angle

cone has 1 seed (hidden by bracts) x2

young branch tips

Death Valley Ephedra

branches erect; 2 scales at each joint

x2 female cone has 2 seeds

male cone

x2

Green Ephedra

branches about 45° angle

2 scales at each joint

x2

cone has 2 seeds

Nevada Ephedra

This strange plant grows in desert regions in both the eastern and western hemispheres and many kinds have been described. For five thousand years a tea made from one of the species was used in China to relieve congestion of the lungs and now the extracted drug, ephedrine, is used all over the world for that purpose. Our American species contain little ephedrine but do contain other chemicals which give flavor to a palatable tea. The Indians, the early settlers and people of the present day either like this brew or feel it is good for their health.

DEATH VALLEY EPHEDRA   *Ephedra funerea*   Ephedra family

Once you have learned the characteristic look of the *genus* ephedra you can always recognize it, but the recognition of the *kind* of ephedra you are looking at is not always so easy. Death Valley ephedra fortunately has a typical growth habit. The short gray-green stems spread in a whorl from the main axis at an angle of about sixty degrees. The presence of three scale-like leaves is a very important character, but often these minute strawlike appendages have weathered off. Usually only one seed develops in each of the small "cones," while in the other two ephedras listed here the seeds are paired instead of single. This species grows on both sides of Death Valley and in adjacent Nevada.

UPPER DESERT SLOPES AND VALLEY FLOOR AND FANS; SHRUB

GREEN EPHEDRA (MORMON TEA)   *Ephedra viridis*   Ephedra family

The green ephedra grows on rocky canyon slopes and on mesas in the pinyon-juniper area or even in the upper part of the creosote-bush belt. The bushes are three or four feet high and not quite as broad, and the stems are beset with many erect, bright green, broom-like branches. The slightly thickened "joints" are dark and the two tiny leaf scales break off in age. The male and female flowers of this strange gymnosperm are borne on different plants.

PINYON-JUNIPER WOODLAND; SHRUB

NEVADA EPHEDRA   *Ephedra nevadensis*   Ephedra family

This is a low gray-green shrub with short straggly branches sticking out in all directions from the nodes, at an angle of about forty-five degrees. This kind of ephedra is widespread and is found from eastern Oregon and from Utah south to eastern California and western Arizona. Other species grow in the Death Valley area.

UPPER DESERT SLOPES; SHRUB

BUD SAGEBRUSH   *Artemisia spinescens*   Sunflower family

The bud sagebrush is a small compact shrub usually less than a foot high, much shorter than its associates, horsebush *(Tetradymia)*, white brittlebush *(Encelia farinosa)*, spiny menodora and others. It is leafless in winter—a rather spiny shrub, grayish with scales above and with shreddy bark on the older portion. The spines, which are an inch or more long, are really the flowering branches of preceding years. In spring the plant is covered with short divided cobwebby leaves and small yellowish green flower heads, and gives forth that pleasant sagebrush odor. Bud sagebrush grows commonly in the Great Basin and the adjacent Rocky Mountain region.

UPPER DESERT SLOPES; SHRUB

BIG SAGEBRUSH   *Artemisia tridentata*   Sunflower family

Sagebrush, tall or short, makes its presence known by its tangy aroma, which is especially noticeable after a shower. There is not the vast acreage of big sagebrush in Death Valley National Monument that there is on the plains of the northwest, though it is abundant at higher elevations in the mountains of Death Valley. There it is usually much dwarfed. If one did not include the flowering stems with their multitude of tiny rayless flowers in measuring the height, the shrubs would be said to be only a few inches tall and look like gnarled miniature trees. The larger plants at a lower elevation have the same habit. There are two species of the dwarfed sagebrushes, the low form of the big sagebrush and the low sagebrush *(Artemisia nova)*. They resemble each other and are separated on quite technical details. The most obvious differences between the two are the shorter flower heads and the leaves which are one and one-half to three times as long as they are wide in the latter, while in the big sagebrush the leaves are three to six times as long as wide.

PINYON-JUNIPER, LIMBER-BRISTLECONE PINE WOODLAND; SHRUB

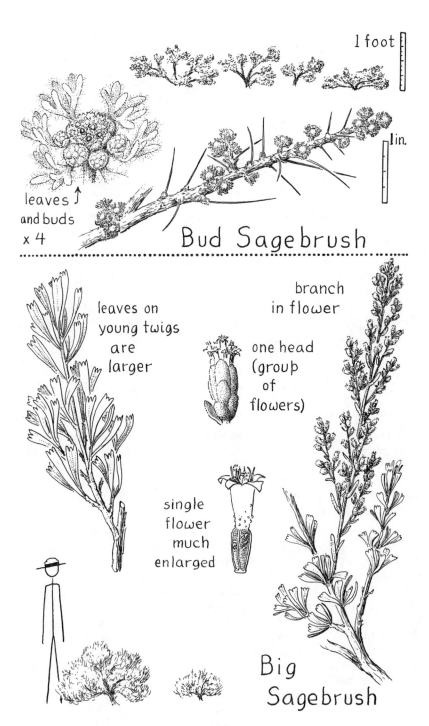

1 foot

1 in.

leaves
and buds
x 4

leaves

Bud Sagebrush

leaves on
young twigs
are
larger

branch
in flower

one head
(group
of
flowers)

single
flower
much
enlarged

Big
Sagebrush

131

PRICKLE-LEAF   *Hecastocleis shockleyi*   Sunflower family

This is a rare plant in Death Valley and not too common in its rather restricted range—southwestern Nevada and adjacent mountains in the Death Valley region—where proper growing conditions are to be found. It would seem from the scant data on the labels on the few botanical specimens that prickle-leaf thrives best on soils derived from a limestone. It has been collected in the Grapevine Mountains in upper Titus Canyon at an altitude where one would expect junipers.

There is only one kind (species) of prickle-leaf and Asa Gray at Harvard in 1882 honored the collector William H. Shockley by naming the specimens submitted *Hecastocleis shockleyi*. Shockley was a mining engineer living in southwestern Nevada whose hobby was plant collecting. Several species that also occur across the California border were gathered the first time by him.

It forms a rounded, much-branched shrub—1-½ to 3 feet tall and wide, with foliage of yellowish green color instead of the common desert gray. The leaves are narrow, firm, and strongly spine-tipped. Several oval, straw-colored bracts that have prickly margins terminate the branches. Each one of the bracts partly encloses a flower head. These heads (involucres) differ from those usually seen in the sunflower family because they have but a single flower in a single head instead of about 5 to more than 150 flowers per head, as one sees in thistles, asters, rabbit-brush, and others. The flowers are often parasitized by insects, and good seeds are hard to find.

PINYON-JUNIPER WOODLAND; SHRUB

132

JUNIPER MISTLETOE   *Phoradendron bolleanum densum*
Mistletoe family

Mistletoes never get their feet on the ground. Juniper trees in the mountains are often parasitized and their branches can be killed by over-infestation. Once started, mistletoes can partially maintain themselves as the green color of stems and leaves testifies. The leaves are one inch long or less, and if you want to see what the flower is like, use a hand lens. They are in small spikes and have no petals. Male and female flowers are separated from each other but each has in common three sepals that cover either anthers or pistil. The white berries are juniper mistletoe's only claim to beauty, but the birds love the berries for food. New infestations of this woody plant can be started by their eating habits.

At least one other species of mistletoe is found in parts of the monument. *Phoradendron californicum* (mesquite mistletoe) grows on mesquite, has leaves that are reduced to mere scales, and has translucent coral berries. The inflorescence in contrast to juniper mistletoe is longer but the flowers themselves are equally obscure.

PINYON-JUNIPER WOODLAND; SHRUBBY PARASITE

133

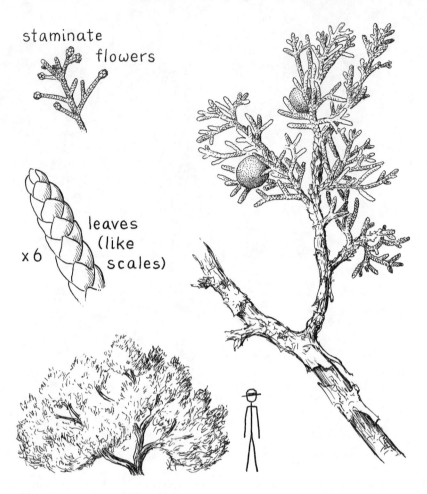

staminate flowers

leaves (like scales)

x6

UTAH JUNIPER   *Juniperus osteosperma*   Cypress family

The juniper and the pinyon pine form a belt on the higher mountains in Death Valley, roughly between the 5,000 and 7,500 foot levels, because it is around this elevation that the summer and winter temperatures, drainage, soil, and precipitation meet the growing needs of the trees. If Joshua trees were common in Death Valley, instead of occurring but rarely, they would begin below the lowest junipers and extend downward about 2,000 feet, as the growing conditions at that level would be right for them. Climate is a prime factor in the distribution of species but many other factors have to be studied, too. That is why the distribution of plants is so fascinating. Utah juniper is a native of the mountain ranges of the Great Basin. It was useful, also, to the Panamint Indians, so Coville reported. They used the wood to make their bows.

PINYON-JUNIPER WOODLAND; TREE

134

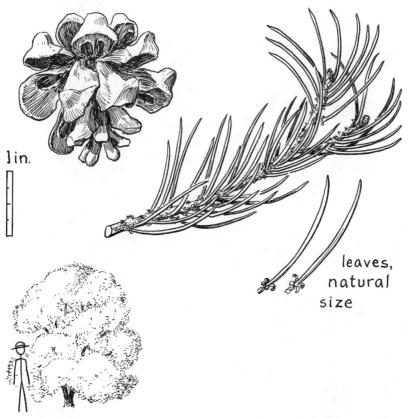

leaves,
natural
size

1 in.

SINGLELEAF PINYON PINE   *Pinus monophylla*   Pine family

In the days when the Indians were the only inhabitants in Death Valley, pine nuts and mesquite pods were their most dependable source of food, but now the gathering of pine nuts there is done by the jays. Even today Indians of the Great Basin area do a bit of harvesting of the nuts, though more as a source of income than of food. The trees are branching, usually with a divided trunk, and grow to a height of 15 to 45 feet. They usually grow at a higher elevation than the junipers with which they are associated. The wood of the pinyons furnished the source of the charcoal which formerly was made in the beehive-shaped kilns which are still standing in upper Wildrose Canyon. There are several species of the pinyon pine in southwestern United States and Mexico. The most obvious difference between them is the number of needles in the clusters, which may have one, two, three, or four per cluster. The two-needle pinyon *(Pinus edulis)* and the four-needle one *(Pinus quadrifolia)* barely reach the borders of California.

PINYON-JUNIPER WOODLAND; TREE

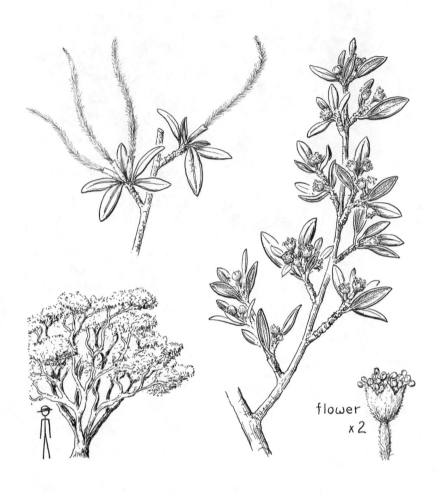

flower
x2

CURLLEAF MOUNTAIN-MAHOGANY
Cercocarpus ledifolius   Rose family

Mountain-mahogany is a conspicuous part of the pinyon pine woodland. In other places in its wide western distribution it is sometimes found at higher elevations. It is 15 to 25 feet tall and though it is bushy in habit, its sturdy furrowed trunk and stout rough branches give it the dignity of a tree. The wood is very hard. The lance-shaped leaves are thick in texture and are dark green above and pale below. Mountain-mahogany belongs to the rose family and is one of the members that have no petals on the flowers. The long white furry tails of the fruits give it eye appeal.

PINYON-JUNIPER WOODLAND; TREE

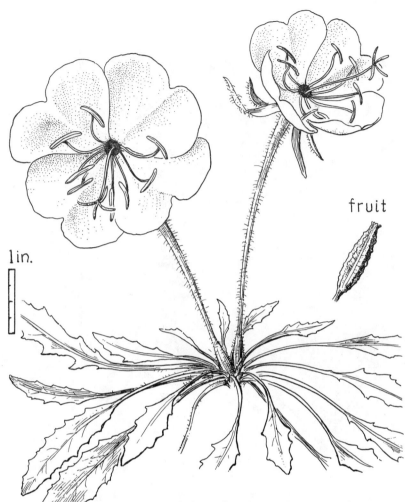

fruit

1 in.

TUFTED EVENING-PRIMROSE *Oenothera caespitosa marginata*
Evening-primrose family

Many kinds of evening-primroses with flowers large and small grow in many places in the monument but this is one of the largest. This perennial, found at high elevations, has no stem at all, only a flat cluster of leaves with toothed edges from which rise the fragrant white flowers which are at least two inches broad. They appear to be growing on stalks, but what seems to be a stalk is only the tube of the flower, which is attached to the woody oval seed-bearing capsule down on the ground in the rosette of leaves. It grows in similar places in the west.

**LIMBER-BRISTLECONE PINE AND PINYON-JUNIPER WOODLAND;
HERB; WHITE**

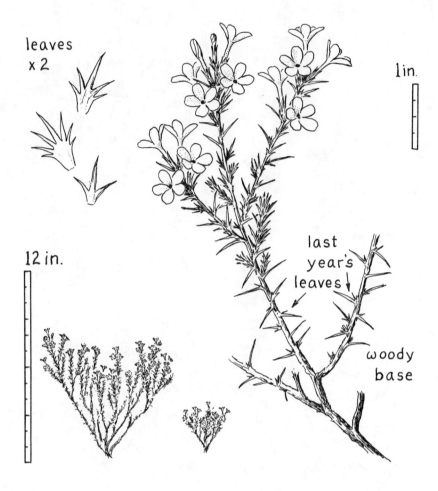

leaves
x 2

1 in.

12 in.

last
year's
leaves

woody
base

GRANITE GILIA   *Leptodactylon pungens*   Phlox family

Three other genera of the phlox family have species illustrated in this book. At least two other genera and many other species occur in Death Valley but are not seen on these pages. Granite gilia reminds one of the prostrate phloxes of the alpine areas of the western mountains but it has a more nearly bushy habit, and the lobes of the white corollas spread like a funnel instead of spreading at right angles as do those of the phloxes. The leaves are small and needlesharp and are set densely along the stems. This variant of granite gilia is found among the pinyon pines and is perhaps more common even at higher elevations where the limber and bristlecone pines are at home.

LIMBER-BRISTLECONE PINE AND PINYON-JUNIPER WOODLAND;
HERB; WHITE

138

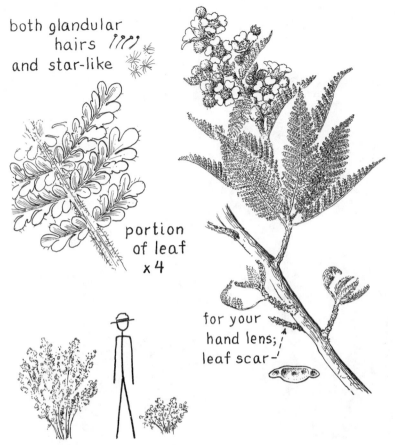

both glandular
hairs
and star-like

portion
of leaf
x 4

for your
hand lens;
leaf scar

TANSYBUSH (DESERTSWEET)　　*Chamaebatiaria millefolium*
Rose family

　　Shrubs or trees of the rose family are well represented in the
pinyon-juniper and limber-bristlecone pine areas. Within an altitudinal range of 5,000 feet, at least a dozen different shrubs belonging to the rose family have been collected in the monument. Some
occur commonly; others are rarely seen—service berry, for example.
About the line where the limber pines begin, and also in the pinyon
belt, the erect several-stemmed bushes of the tansybush are to be
found. The bushes are two and a half to five feet high, with several
erect stems which are copiously clothed with thickened, somewhat
sticky, fernlike leaves that exude a pleasant aromatic fragrance. The
white flowers, though small (about one-half inch broad), grow in
clusters on the tops of the branches and are conspicuous by their
abundance. It is interesting to note that another good-sized shrub
of the rose family, the rock spiraea *(Holodiscus dumosus)* is often found
growing with it.

LIMBER-BRISTLECONE PINE WOODLAND; SHRUB; WHITE

18 in.

1 in.

Penstemons are natives of the northern hemisphere but the greatest number of species is to be found in western North America. Many kinds are grown in gardens, as they are hardy perennials (rarely shrubs) with attractively colored flowers of many different shades. The desert is not without its quota of species, though more are found in wetter climes.

BRIDGES PENSTEMON   *Penstemon bridgesii*   Figwort family

This scarlet penstemon is found in rocky ground where the pine trees grow, among the pinyons as well as those of higher elevations. The plants are a foot or two high. The yellow-green leaves are narrow and more abundant at the base of the plant. The flowers, of which there are several on the flower stalk, are an inch or an inch and one-half long and rather narrow, and the lower lip is sharply rolled back and split into three lobes. Bridges penstemon is widespread in the mountains of the west.

LIMBER-BRISTLECONE PINE AND PINYON-JUNIPER WOODLAND; HERB; RED

140

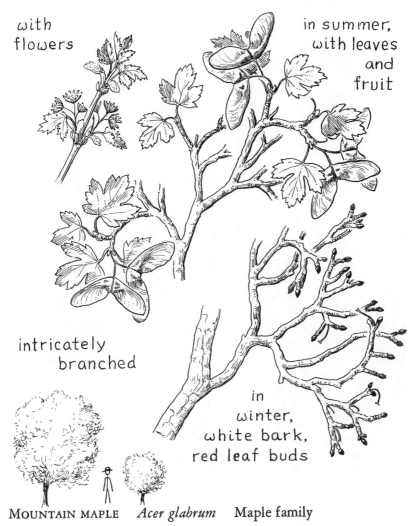

with
flowers

in summer,
with leaves
and
fruit

intricately
branched

in
winter,
white bark,
red leaf buds

MOUNTAIN MAPLE   *Acer glabrum*   Maple family

In the high canyons of the Panamints, high enough to be in the area where the limber pines grow, a desert form of the maple tree is found. This desert form of the mountain maple *(Acer glabrum diffusum)* is not uncommon in desert ranges of southern California, Nevada and northern Arizona. The trees are 8 to 20 feet tall and have a rather bushy growth. In spring the small maple leaves, which are about one inch long and wide, unfold and the small reddish flowers bloom with them. By summer the winged paired seeds have developed. They fall in autumn with the yellowed leaves and the cycle is completed in winter with the startlingly white, leafless twigs and branches which bear the tiny red leafbuds of the next season.

LIMBER-BRISTLECONE PINE WOODLAND; SMALL TREE; RED

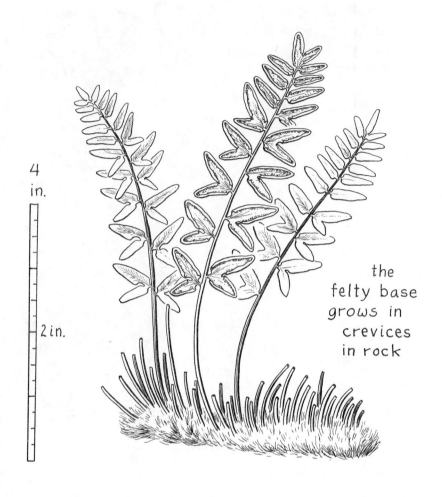

4
in.

2 in.

the
felty base
grows in
crevices
in rock

BREWERS CLIFFBRAKE   *Pellaea breweri*   Fern family

High up in the Panamints where the limber and bristlecone
pines grow one finds the short, densely tufted, bright green fronds
of the Brewers cliffbrake among the rocks. Though short in stature,
the fronds, with their closely set, two-parted pinnae, are conspicuous
early in the season. Later they cannot be found, as the stems (stipes)
snap off above the brown felty base buried among the rocks. The
cliffbrake is a fern of the western mountains from Montana south.

LIMBER- BRISTLECONE PINE WOODLAND; FERN

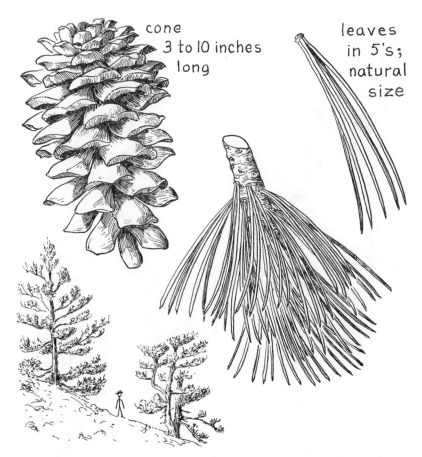

cone
3 to 10 inches
long

leaves
in 5's;
natural
size

Very few kinds of the trees growing in Death Valley National Monument are natives of the region. One might say that the tamarisks, the palms and such have been planted in self-defense against the sun. As is to be expected, the three pines that are natives grow at rather high elevations. The singleleaf pinyon will be met with more commonly, as it grows on mesas and slopes, mostly within the 5,000 to 7,000 foot levels, usually not too far from roads. But to see the bristlecone and the limber pines one walks, as these grow high on the slopes of the Panamints. Specimens have been collected at 11,000 feet.

LIMBER PINE   *Pinus flexilis*   Pine family

The cones of the limber pine are larger than those of the Great Basin bristlecone pine, and the scales spread almost at right angles. The needles are also in bundles of five but are longer and not so densely set.

LIMBER-BRISTLECONE PINE WOODLAND; TREE

143

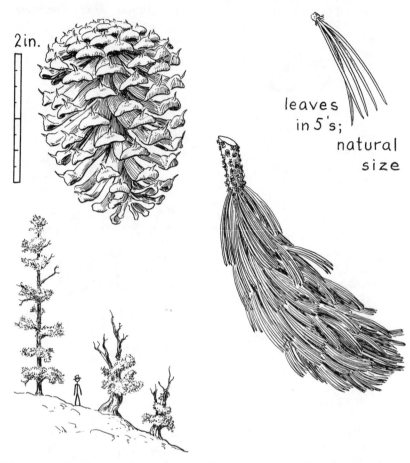

2 in.

leaves
in 5's;
natural
size

GREAT BASIN BRISTLECONE PINE   *Pinus longaeva*   Pine family

Until 1970, these trees were known as *Pinus aristata,* the name
given to similar specimens in the Rocky Mountains. It now appears that
the bristlecone pines of the Great Basin ranges are a separate species.
Hence the new name. The scales of the cones, which are from two and
one-half to three and one-half inches long, bear an incurved prickle—
hence the name "bristlecone." The short needles which are in bundles
of five densely clothe the somewhat pendent branchlets, and are long-
persistent. Some specimens of this species of pine tested for their age
have been found to reach the almost unbelievable figure of 4,000 years
and over.

LIMBER-BRISTLECONE PINE WOODLAND; TREE

INDEX OF PLANT NAMES

Common names that consist of more than one word are to be sought under the last word. For example, lupines, such as Arizona lupine, yelloweye lupine are under lupine in alphabetical order. Compound names spelled as a single word such as desert gold, or names that are hyphenated, such as desert-star, are listed under the initial letter, "D" in this case.

Names of plant families in front of book

146